The Thyroid Cure COOKBOOK

The Thyroid Cure COOKBOOK

More Than 80 Nourishing Recipes to Restore Your Body to Complete Health

RODALE.

© 2016 by Rodale Inc.

Photographs © 2016 by Rodale Inc.

Cover photos (*clockwise from top left*): Seared Carrots (*page 120*); Tuscan Country Chicken (*page 90*); and Beef Stew with Root Vegetables (*page 38*)

Photographs by Mitch Mandel/Rodale Images

Book design by Christina Gaugler

Library of Congress Cataloging-in-Publication Data is on file with the publisher.

ISBN 978-1-62336-820-3   direct mail paperback

2 4 6 8 10 9 7 5 3   direct mail paperback

We inspire health, healing, happiness, and love in the world.
Starting with you.

Contents

INTRODUCTION

When you're starting on a health journey, you want to eat foods that not only feed your body, but also nourish your soul. Welcome to *The Thyroid Cure Cookbook*, chock-full of recipes to help you eat clean and restore your health.

You may be struggling with the nagging feeling that something isn't quite right—and your doctor has told you it may have to do with your thyroid function or an autoimmune disorder. Or you might just be looking to cleanse your body of impurities. Or you may just want some flavorful and nutritious recipe ideas. Whatever your reason, this cookbook is for you. Eating these foods will likely help you lose weight, increase your energy, make your skin and hair radiant, improve your sleep, lift your mood, and most importantly, eliminate your chronic autoimmune symptoms.

You'll find more than 80 healing recipes, a 1-week meal plan, and a shopping list. Every recipe in this book is easy to make, is wonderfully appetizing, and contains an abundance of just what you need to purge impurities. These dishes are also deeply gratifying. Breakfast recipes like the Asparagus and Mushroom Rice Bowl (page 21) and the Avocado Egg Boat (page 23) will make your stomach happy and leave your body full of energy all day long.

Not only will you find hearty lunches like Thai Squash Soup (page 47) and decadent dinners like Lamb Lollipops (page 81), but you'll also want to cook up mouthwatering side dishes like Rosemary Sweet Potato Wedges (page 134) and Garlic-Marinated Mushrooms Topped with Avocado (page 115)—perfect savory accompaniments to any meal. Or you may want to try the Roasted Butternut Squash Skewers with Rosemary Dip (page 61), which consist of only six ingredients and are ready in just 45 minutes.

If you've read through *The Thyroid Cure*, you understand the importance of cleansing your system. Those who suffer from autoimmune diseases are particularly sensitive to toxic substances, which cause your liver to become overburdened. The only solution is to quit adding to that dangerous toxic load, so choose organic ingredients whenever possible. *The Thyroid Cure Cookbook* is just what you need to get started eating clean now.

These foods are nourishing and will not irritate your body. They will leave you feeling wonderful from the inside out. Good health begins with what you feed your body, and what you feed your body has an enormous impact on how you feel. Prepare to feel vibrantly healthy and better than ever.

Best of luck to you on your wellness journey.

ASPARAGUS AND MUSHROOM RICE BOWL (page 21)

Rise and Shine

COCONUT YOGURT WITH BLACKBERRIES

Prep Time: 5 minutes
Total Time: 5 minutes

SERVINGS: 1

Complete with a smooth, tangy taste, dairy-free coconut yogurt is an excellent alternative to cow's milk yogurt. Sprinkle in blackberries for a breakfast so sweet that you'll think you're eating dessert.

8 ounces homemade plain coconut yogurt (page 31)

½ cup fresh blackberries

Alternate layers of the yogurt and the berries in a dish and serve.

Nutrition Information: 546 calories, 7 g protein, 19 g carbohydrates, 4 g fiber, 9 g sugar, 49 g fat, 46 g saturated fat, 76 mg sodium

COCONUT YOGURT WITH RASPBERRIES

Prep Time: 5 minutes
Total Time: 5 minutes

SERVINGS: 1

Coconut and raspberries are both notorious for having a high fiber content, which means they pack a powerful punch when paired. Add zest to your filling, fiber-full breakfast by tossing the raspberries in lemon juice before serving.

½ cup fresh red raspberries

1 teaspoon fresh lemon juice

8 ounces homemade plain coconut yogurt (page 31)

1. In a small bowl, toss the raspberries with the lemon juice.

2. Alternate layers of the yogurt and the raspberries in a small bowl and serve.

Nutrition Information: 533 calories, 7 g protein, 20 g carbohydrates, 4 g fiber, 9 g sugar, 47 g fat, 49 g saturated fat, 75 mg sodium

HONEYED SUMMER FRUIT BOWL

Prep Time: 20 minutes
Total Time: 50 minutes

SERVINGS: 8

This colorful breakfast bowl is jam-packed with the flavor and nutrients you need to kick-start your day. To save time, prepare the fruit and honey dressing the night before and wake up to flavor-infused fruit. For maximum antioxidants, sip organic green tea with this dish.

2½ tablespoons honey

1 tablespoon lemon juice

Pinch of ground cinnamon

2 medium nectarines, cut into thin wedges

2 medium peaches, cut into thin wedges

2 large plums, cut into thin wedges

1 cup blueberries

1. In a large bowl, combine the honey, lemon juice, and cinnamon. Add the nectarines, peaches, plums, and blueberries.

2. Toss just until the fruit is well mixed and coated with the honey mixture.

3. Let stand for 30 minutes before serving, to allow the flavors to blend.

Nutrition Information (per serving): 69 calories, 1 g protein, 17 g carbohydrates, 2 g fiber, 15 g sugar, 0 g fat, 0 g saturated fat, 1 mg sodium

SAVORY RICE PORRIDGE

This warm, savory porridge is a perfect comfort breakfast on a lazy Sunday morning. The rice soaks up the runny egg yolk, making it mushy and sweet, while the wilted spinach adds a flavorful crunch. The best part? It can be made in just 10 minutes.

2 cups cooked organic brown rice, warmed*

1 cup fresh spinach

1 tablespoon extra-virgin olive oil

2 eggs

Salt

Pepper

1. Divide the warm rice between 2 bowls and top each with ½ cup of the spinach.

2. In a medium skillet over medium heat, warm the oil. Add the eggs, and when the whites are opaque, carefully turn them without breaking the yolks.

3. Cook for 10 seconds.

4. Top each bowl's spinach with an over-easy egg and season with the salt and pepper. The spinach will wilt under the egg. Serve immediately.

Made from parboiled whole grain brown rice, 10-minute brown rice is a quick alternative to traditional brown rice, which can take 30 to 40 minutes to cook.

Nutrition Information (per serving): 355 calories, 11 g protein, 48 g carbohydrates, 4 g fiber, 0 g sugar, 13 g fat, 3 g saturated fat, 165 mg sodium

FRUIT BOWL WITH AVOCADO

Prep Time: 10 minutes
Cook Time: 10 minutes
Total Time: 20 minutes

SERVINGS: 2

Here's a quick, tasty meal that's easy to put together for breakfast or to save for a sweet midmorning snack. This unexpectedly smooth dish is loaded with healthy fats from the avocado, which will also fill you up the nutritious way.

2 teaspoons honey

2 tablespoons fresh lime juice

1 tablespoon extra-virgin olive oil

1 teaspoon coarsely ground black pepper, plus more for serving

1 ripe plum, pitted and cut into wedges

1 ripe nectarine, pitted and cut into wedges

1 ripe peach, pitted and cut into wedges

6 ounces fresh raspberries

1 ripe Hass avocado, pitted and diced

¼ cup small red or green basil leaves

1. In a large bowl, whisk together the honey, lime juice, oil, and pepper.

2. Add the plum, nectarine, peach, raspberries, and avocado to the bowl. Toss to coat with the dressing.

3. Let sit for 10 minutes to meld the flavors, then serve with more pepper and the basil leaves.

Nutrition Information (per serving): 326 calories, 4 g protein, 42 g carbohydrates, 13 g fiber, 25 g sugar, 19 g fat, 3 g saturated fat, 7 mg sodium

GRILLED PEACHES

Prep Time: 6 minutes
Cook Time: 6 minutes
Total Time: 12 minutes

SERVINGS: 4

Grilled peaches may seem like a summertime cookout staple, but they also make for a deliciously sweet breakfast. If you don't have a grill, place the peaches on a grill pan on your stove and cook for the same amount of time.

1 tablespoon extra-virgin olive oil

1 tablespoon lemon juice

2 peaches, halved

¼ teaspoon cinnamon

Pinch of ground black pepper

1. In a small bowl, whisk together the oil and lemon juice and brush it over the peaches. Season with the cinnamon and pepper.

2. Grill the peaches for 3 minutes, turn, and grill for 3 minutes.

3. Remove the peaches from the heat and let them cool. Serve immediately.

Nutrition Information (per serving): 50 calories, 1 g protein, 5 g carbohydrates, 1 g fiber, 4 g sugar, 3 g fat, 6 g saturated fat, 0 mg sodium

SWEET POTATO PANCAKES

Prep Time: 15 minutes
Cook Time: 20 minutes
Total Time: 35 minutes

SERVINGS: 2

Traditional potato pancakes are made with white potatoes, but swapping in sweet potatoes provides an extra boost of fiber. Dip the pancakes in applesauce, which is a great, healthy alternative to the sugar found in most baked goods.

1 large sweet potato, peeled

2 scallions, chopped

2 egg whites

⅛ teaspoon freshly ground black pepper

Pinch of grated nutmeg

2 teaspoons extra-virgin olive oil, divided

1 cup unsweetened applesauce

1. Grate the potato into a large bowl.

2. Add the scallions, egg whites, pepper, and nutmeg, and mix to combine.

3. Heat 1 teaspoon of the oil in a nonstick skillet over medium heat.

4. Drop the potato mixture by ¼ cupful into the skillet to make 3 pancakes. Flatten them into 3" rounds. Cook for 6 to 8 minutes, turning once, or until the pancakes are golden brown.

5. Transfer the pancakes to a plate and cover to keep them warm. Heat the remaining 1 teaspoon of oil and cook the remaining potato mixture to make 6 pancakes total.

6. Serve the pancakes with the applesauce.

Nutrition Information (per serving): 192 calories, 24 g protein, 3 g carbohydrates, 1 g fiber, 2 g sugar, 9 g fat, 2 g saturated fat, 88 mg sodium

THE NEW AMERICAN OMELET

Prep Time: 7 minutes
Cook Time: 10 minutes
Total Time: 17 minutes

SERVINGS: 2

If you struggle with eating your veggies, omelets are a terrific way to sneak in some greens. This omelet is loaded with vitamins A, C, and K, which are good for your eyes, skin, immune system, and heart health.

5 eggs

2 tablespoons chopped flat-leaf parsley

2 teaspoons extra-virgin olive oil

½ cup spinach

¼ cup chopped broccoli florets

5 spears asparagus, chopped

¼ cup halved green beans

1 clove garlic, finely chopped

Dash of black pepper

1. In a medium bowl, beat the eggs and parsley together.

2. Coat a skillet with the olive oil and place it over medium heat. Add the spinach, broccoli, asparagus, green beans, garlic, and pepper to the skillet and sauté for 5 minutes.

3. Pour the egg mixture over the vegetables. Stir for about 30 seconds and then let it sit for 1 minute.

4. Stir again until the eggs firm up and let the mixture sit for another minute. Fold it and serve immediately.

Nutrition Information (per serving): 240 calories, 18 g protein, 5 g carbohydrates, 2 g fiber, 2 g sugar, 17 g fat, 5 g saturated fat, 209 mg sodium

LOX, EGGS, AND ONIONS

Prep Time: 5 minutes
Cook Time: 8 minutes
Total Time: 13 minutes

SERVINGS: 4

With salmon and eggs, you're eating an impressive breakfast that's rich in omega-3s and healthy fats. But make sure to compare labels when buying salmon; some types of lox, or smoked salmon, contain loads of excess salt.

1 teaspoon extra-virgin olive oil

1 medium yellow onion, finely chopped

4 ounces smoked salmon, sliced into thin strips

4 large eggs or 8 egg whites or 1 cup egg substitute

¼ cup sliced scallions

1. Heat a large skillet over medium heat. Add the oil.

2. Add the onion and cook for 1 minute.

3. Add the salmon and cook for about 2 minutes, or until it begins to turn opaque and lighter in color.

4. In a small bowl, whisk together the eggs. Add them to the skillet.

5. Cook the egg mixture for about 5 minutes, or until it is firm and almost dry, stirring to cook evenly.

6. Top each serving with 1 tablespoon of the scallions and serve.

Nutrition Information (per serving): 192 calories, 24 g protein, 3 g carbohydrates, 1 g fiber, 2 g sugar, 9 g fat, 2 g saturated fat, 88 mg sodium

GRILLED STEAK AND EGGS

Prep Time: 5 minutes
Cook Time: 12 minutes
Total Time: 17 minutes

SERVINGS: 4

Steak and eggs isn't just meant for body builders. When prepared correctly and with the right ingredients, a high-protein breakfast like this one is extraordinarily heart healthy. Buy organic, lean cuts of beef and use omega-3-enriched eggs—they've been proven to prevent heart disease.

¼ teaspoon freshly ground black pepper

¼ teaspoon salt-free onion powder

8 ounces sirloin steak

2 tablespoons + 2 teaspoons extra-virgin olive oil

16 cups fresh spinach

4 eggs

1. Rub the pepper and onion powder onto the steak.
2. In a grill pan, heat 1 teaspoon of the oil over medium-high heat.
3. Grill the steak for 6 minutes, turning once, or until a thermometer inserted in the center registers 145°F for medium-rare. Let the steak rest for 10 minutes before slicing.
4. Meanwhile, in a large skillet, heat 2 tablespoons of the oil over low heat. Add the spinach to the pan and cook for 1 minute, or until it begins to wilt. Divide the spinach among 4 plates.
5. Heat the remaining 1 teaspoon of oil in the skillet over medium-low heat.
6. Crack the eggs into the skillet. Cook for 3 minutes, or until the egg whites are set.
7. Serve the eggs with soft yolks, or cover and cook them for 2 minutes, or until the yolks are cooked through. Top each serving of spinach with 1 egg and serve with the sliced steak.

Nutrition Information (per serving): 246 calories, 21 g protein, 3 g carbohydrates, 2 g fiber, 1 g sugar, 17 g fat, 4 g saturated fat, 160 mg sodium

SMOKED SALMON BREAKFAST SCRAMBLE

Prep Time: 3 minutes
Cook Time: 8 minutes
Total Time: 11 minutes

SERVINGS: 4

Leftover fish makes for a tasty breakfast. Mix the salmon in with some eggs and spices for a flavorful addition to a weekend brunch. Don't be afraid to throw some mixed greens or asparagus into the scramble for added nutrients.

4 eggs

Salt

Freshly ground black pepper

½ cup flaked smoked salmon

2 tablespoons sliced chives

1. In a small bowl, whisk the eggs. Season with salt and pepper to taste.
2. Coat a skillet with cooking spray and place it over medium heat.
3. Add the eggs and reduce the heat to medium-low. Stir frequently but gently, pushing the eggs from the pan edges into the center.
4. Add the salmon and stir it into the mixture.
5. Remove the eggs from the heat when just set. Serve immediately, topped with the chives.

Nutrition Information (per serving): 130 calories, 17 g protein, 0 g carbohydrates, 0 g fiber, 0 g sugar, 7 g fat, 2 g saturated fat, 116 mg sodium

THREE-EGG VEGETABLE OMELET

Prep Time: 10 minutes
Cook Time: 5 minutes
Total Time: 15 minutes

SERVINGS: 1

Omelets are the perfect place to experiment with new vegetables. Zucchini is high in fiber and is known to help fight colon cancer, while mushrooms are proven protectors against cardiovascular disease and healthy sources of B vitamins (aka energy boosters), making them the perfect breakfast veggie.

3 eggs

¼ cup chopped mushrooms

¼ cup chopped zucchini

Salt

Freshly ground black pepper

1. Coat a large skillet with olive oil cooking spray and place it over medium heat.
2. In a small bowl, beat the eggs well. Add the eggs to the skillet, allowing them to coat the bottom of the pan. Cook for 3 minutes, or until the bottom begins to set.
3. Top one half of the omelet with the mushrooms, zucchini, salt, and pepper.
4. Carefully fold the remaining half over the filling and cook for 2 minutes, or until cooked through.

Nutrition Information: 224 calories, 20 g protein, 3 g carbohydrates, 0.5 g fiber, 2 g sugar, 14 g fat, 5 g saturated fat, 216 mg sodium

ASPARAGUS AND MUSHROOM RICE BOWL

Prep Time: 10 minutes
Cook Time: 10 minutes
Total Time: 20 minutes

SERVINGS: 4

Just ½ cup of cooked, chopped asparagus packs 57 percent of your daily requirement of vitamin K, which promotes bone and heart health. Mushrooms provide B vitamins, copper, and the antioxidant mineral selenium, while also adding a savory flavor to the dish.

Rice Bowl

2 cups 10-minute brown rice*

1 tablespoon + 1 teaspoon extra-virgin olive oil

1 pound asparagus, trimmed and cut into 1" pieces

8 ounces sliced cremini mushrooms

4 large eggs

Dressing

3 tablespoons extra-virgin olive oil

Juice of ½ lemon

2 tablespoons finely chopped fresh dill

1 clove garlic, minced

½ teaspoon salt

¼ teaspoon freshly ground black pepper

1. *To make the rice bowl:* Cook the rice according to the package directions. Meanwhile, in a large skillet, heat 1 tablespoon of the oil over medium heat. Add the asparagus and mushrooms and cook for 5 minutes, or until the mushrooms have softened and darkened and the asparagus is just tender. Transfer to a bowl and set aside. Return the skillet to the heat and add the remaining 1 teaspoon of oil. Add the eggs and cook for 3 minutes. Flip the eggs and cook for 30 seconds, or until they reach your desired level of doneness. Transfer to a plate and cover with foil to keep warm.

2. *To make the dressing:* In a small bowl, whisk together the oil, lemon juice, dill, garlic, salt, and pepper.

3. Divide the rice among 4 bowls. Top each with a portion of the vegetables and 1 egg. Drizzle with the dressing.

Made from parboiled whole grain brown rice, 10-minute brown rice is a quick alternative to traditional brown rice, which can take 30 to 40 minutes to cook.

Nutrition Information (per serving): 385 calories, 13 g protein, 39 g carbohydrates, 4 g fiber, 2 g sugar:, 21 g fat, 3 g saturated fat, 371 mg sodium

MORNING RICE BOWL

This rice bowl combines all of your favorite fall vegetables with eggs for a hearty breakfast that's perfect for chilly mornings. Make sure that you allow time to poach your egg and cook the rice, sweet potato, beet, and acorn squash in advance—or use already-cooked leftovers! And there's an added bonus: Studies show that dieters who have eggs for breakfast shed more pounds than those who eat a bagel.

⅔ cup cooked organic brown rice*

½ cooked sweet potato, sliced

1 cooked beet, sliced

¼ cup cooked acorn squash, chopped

1 poached egg (refer to page 60 for directions)

1. Cook the rice according to the package directions.

2. In a bowl, combine the rice, sweet potato, beet, and squash.

3. Top with the poached egg and serve immediately.

*Made from parboiled whole grain brown rice, 10-minute brown rice is a quick alternative to traditional brown rice, which can take 30 to 40 minutes to cook.

Nutrition Information: 318 calories, 12 g protein, 54 g carbohydrates, 7 g fiber, 10 g sugar, 6 g fat, 1 g saturated fat, 235 mg sodium

AVOCADO EGG BOAT

Prep Time: 3 minutes
Cook Time: 2 minutes
Total Time: 5 minutes

SERVINGS: 1

An avocado egg boat is the healthy equivalent of the Mickey Mouse pancakes your mom made you as a kid—it's fun to look at and even more fun to eat. Make this as a quick and satisfying breakfast.

½ avocado, pitted and peeled

1 large egg

½ cup raspberries

1. Cut a sliver off the bottom side of the avocado half so it will lie flat and place it in a skillet.

2. Crack the egg into the hole where the pit was, cover the skillet, and cook over low heat for 2 minutes, or to desired doneness.

3. Gently remove the avocado and egg from the skillet and serve with the berries on the side.

Nutrition Information: 264 calories, 9 g protein, 16 g carbohydrates, 11 g fiber, 4 g sugar, 20 g fat, 4 g saturated fat, 79 mg sodium

BLUEBERRY SMOOTHIE

Prep Time: 4 minutes
Total Time: 4 minutes

SERVINGS: 2

The yogurt in this smoothie provides you with good bacteria that promote healthy digestion, while the blueberries load you up with heart-friendly nutrients. If the drink is too tart for your taste, add a drop or two of organic honey.

1 cup homemade plain coconut yogurt (page 31)

1 cup frozen, unsweetened blueberries

1. In a blender, combine the yogurt and blueberries. Blend for 1 minute, or until smooth.

2. Transfer to a glass and serve immediately.

Nutrition Information (per serving): 297 calories, 3 g protein, 16 g carbohydrates, 2 g fiber, 10 g sugar, 25 g fat, 23 g saturated fat, 39 mg sodium

GREEN SMOOTHIE

Prep Time: 5 minutes
Total Time: 5 minutes

SERVINGS: 2

As is the case with omelets, adding veggies to smoothies is a wonderfully subtle way to increase your veggie intake. The ginger, cardamom, and coconut yogurt combine forces to create the ultimate stomach-soothing smoothie with a delightfully flavorful kick.

1 cup pear, cored and diced

1 cup homemade plain coconut yogurt (page 31)

2 cups baby spinach

2 teaspoons fresh lemon juice

1 teaspoon grated fresh ginger

¼ teaspoon ground cardamom

½ cup ice

1. In a blender, combine the pear, yogurt, spinach, lemon juice, ginger, cardamom, and ice. Blend for 1 to 2 minutes, or until frothy and smooth.

2. Divide between 2 glasses and serve immediately.

Nutrition Information (per serving): 321 calories, 4 g protein, 23 g carbohydrates, 4 g fiber, 12 g sugar, 24 g fat, 23 g saturated fat, 79 mg sodium

CUCUMBER-MINT SMOOTHIE

Kick your seltzer water up a notch by turning it into the perfect poolside drink. The honey and mint transform this drink into a refreshing pick-me-up, while the cucumber benefits your breath: Studies show that cucumber boosts saliva production, which washes away bacteria in your mouth.

1 pound chopped seedless cucumber

½ cup lemon-lime seltzer

⅓ cup chopped fresh mint

¼ cup chopped fresh parsley

4 teaspoons honey

1 tablespoon fresh lemon juice

Parsley, for garnish

1. In a blender, combine the cucumber, seltzer, mint, parsley, honey, and lemon juice. Blend for 1 minute, or until smooth. Strain.

2. Serve immediately with parsley sprigs.

Nutrition Information (per serving): 42 calories, 1 g protein, 11 g carbohydrates, 1 g fiber, 8 g sugar:, 0.2 g fat, 0 g saturated fat, 5 mg sodium

RASPBERRY SMOOTHIE

Prep Time: 5 minutes
Total Time: 3 hours
5 minutes, including time for
freezing

SERVINGS: 1

This tasty raspberry smoothie calls for ginger, which is a proven stomach soother. Ginger is extremely effective at relieving digestive problems such as nausea and pain, and it can even soothe sore muscles after a hard workout.

6 ounces raspberries (about 1 cup)

½ cup homemade plain coconut yogurt (page 31)

1 tablespoon honey

1 teaspoon freshly grated ginger

1. Line a small baking sheet with waxed paper or parchment.

2. Arrange the berries on the pan in a single layer.

3. Freeze until completely frozen, about 3 hours.

4. Transfer the berries to a blender with the yogurt, honey, and ginger. Blend until smooth.

5. Transfer to a glass and serve immediately.

Nutrition Information: 369 calories, 5 g protein, 33 g carbohydrates, 11 g fiber, 16 g sugar, 25 g fat, 23 g saturated fat, 40 mg sodium

THE THYROID CURE HOMEMADE PLAIN COCONUT YOGURT

Prep Time: 5 minutes
Total Time: 12 hours

SERVINGS: 4

You can make this yogurt recipe without a yogurt machine. Just make sure you have a lidded glass jar that's big enough to hold all of the coconut milk from the cans. And be warned that the yogurt will need to sit in the oven for up to 24 hours, so make sure it will be free. Once you've made the yogurt, you may sweeten it with stevia, if you like, or add vanilla extract to taste, if you know you don't react to it.

2 cans (13½ ounces each) full-fat coconut milk (we like Native Forest and Thai Kitchen brands)

2 capsules Klaire Labs Ther-Biotic Complete (We also recommend Pure Encapsulations Probiotics 50B and VSL #3.)

1. Refrigerate the coconut milk overnight to separate the cream from the milk.

2. Scoop the separated cream into a medium bowl. Break open the probiotic capsules and use a whisk or hand mixer to blend their contents into the separated cream until it's smooth.

3. *With a yogurt machine (recommended):* Scoop the probiotic mixture into the sterilized glass jars and place them in the machine for 12 to 15 hours (or follow your machine's directions).

   Without a yogurt machine: Sterilize your glass jar. Place the probiotic mixture in the jar and put the sealed jar of yogurt in the oven with the light on. Close the door and do not turn the oven on. Let the yogurt sit. (The longer it sits, the more yogurt-like it becomes. We recommend 24 hours.)

4. When the yogurt is done, cool it in the refrigerator for a few hours. Set aside 2 tablespoons of yogurt as a culture for your next batch and enjoy the rest of this tangy treat over berries, in place of sour cream, or as a savory sauce.

   Yogurt will last for 5 days in the fridge, but it will continue to culture and it might taste tangier the longer it sits.

Nutrition Information (per serving): 225 calories, 3 g protein, 2 g carbohydrates, 0 g fiber, 3 g sugar, 21 g fat, 20 g saturated fat, 33 mg sodium

BALSAMIC BEETS (page 50)

LUNCH

Midday Fuel-Up

VEGETABLE SOUP

Prep Time: 15 minutes
Cook Time: 25 minutes
Total Time: 40 minutes

SERVINGS: 4

This chunky, nutritious soup is made even better with aromatic rosemary and assertive garlic, which both play very well with mild-mannered zucchini and carrots. To ease the prep, crush the garlic clove with the broad side of a heavy knife—the peel will slip right off.

2 tablespoons extra-virgin olive oil

1 medium yellow onion, chopped

2 medium carrots, thinly sliced

3 cloves garlic, minced

1 tablespoon chopped fresh rosemary or 1 teaspoon dried

¼ teaspoon salt

¼ teaspoon freshly ground black pepper

4 cups low-sodium vegetable or chicken broth

1 small zucchini, chopped

2 tablespoons coconut milk

1. Heat the oil in a large saucepan over medium-high heat.

2. Add the onion, carrots, garlic, rosemary, salt, and pepper. Cook, stirring occasionally, for 5 minutes, or until the vegetables are soft.

3. Stir in the broth. Bring to a boil.

4. Reduce the heat to low, cover, and simmer for 8 minutes.

5. Stir in the zucchini. Cook, covered, for 3 minutes, or until the zucchini is tender. Stir in the coconut milk.

6. Serve immediately or store in an airtight container in your refrigerator for up to 4 days.

Nutrition Information (per serving): 143 calories, 2 g protein, 15 g carbohydrates, 4 g fiber, 4 g sugar, 9 g fat, 2 g saturated fat, 312 mg sodium

FALL SQUASH SOUP

Prep Time: 15 minutes
Cook Time: 60 minutes
Total Time: 1 hour 15 minutes

SERVINGS: 6

All of your favorite autumn flavors are embodied by this hearty soup. The sweet apples pair well with the mellow squash, and the garlic livens up the dish. Plus, research shows that garlic has anti-inflammatory and obesity-fighting properties.

1 large butternut squash, peeled, halved, and seeded, or 9 cups (48 ounces) precut squash

3 medium Mutsu (or Crispin) apples or other cooking apples, peeled, cored, and quartered

1 large onion, cut into chunks

3 cloves garlic, peeled

2 tablespoons extra-virgin olive oil

½ teaspoon salt

½ teaspoon freshly ground black pepper

6 cups reduced-sodium, fat-free chicken or vegetable broth

Parsley, for garnish

1. Preheat the oven to 400°F. Coat 2 large, rimmed baking sheets or a large roasting pan with olive oil cooking spray.

2. Cut the squash into 1½" chunks. Place the squash, apples, onion, and garlic on the prepared baking sheets or pan.

3. Drizzle with the oil and sprinkle with the salt and pepper. Toss to mix well.

4. Roast the vegetables and apples, stirring occasionally, for 40 to 45 minutes, or until very tender. Remove from the oven and let cool briefly.

5. In a food processor, working in batches if necessary, puree the vegetables until smooth. Add broth as needed to thin the mixture.

6. Transfer the puree to a large saucepot and stir in the remaining broth. Warm over medium heat, stirring often, until the soup is piping hot. Garnish with the parsley.

Nutrition Information (per serving): 219 calories, 6 g protein, 43 g carbohydrates, 7 g fiber, 16 g sugar, 5 g fat, 1 g saturated fat, 759 mg sodium

BABY ARTICHOKE STEW

Prep Time: 20 minutes
Cook Time: 30 minutes
Total Time: 50 minutes

SERVINGS: 6

This gorgeous green dish is brimming with antioxidants, vitamins, and nutrients. It pairs extraordinarily well with grilled lamb chops or chicken. Be careful when storing artichokes—they're quite perishable. Place them unwashed in a resealable plastic bag in the refrigerator for no more than 5 days.

1 lemon, halved

12 baby artichokes

Kosher salt

3 tablespoons extra-virgin olive oil

4 baby sweet onions (we used Vidalias), trimmed and very coarsely chopped, or spring onions, white and green parts chopped

½ pound sugar snap peas, trimmed and steamed until tender

1 pound thin to medium asparagus, trimmed, cut diagonally into 3" pieces, and steamed until tender

¼ cup chopped fresh herbs, such as parsley, chervil, and mint

1. Bring a large pot of water to a boil.

2. Squeeze the juice from 1 lemon half into a large bowl of cold water.

3. Trim off the stem and top quarter of each artichoke. Using a sharp paring knife, peel off the outer green leaves until you reach the pale inner leaves. Cut the artichokes in half lengthwise. Place them in the lemon water as you finish trimming them.

4. Squeeze the remaining lemon half into the boiling water and add a pinch of salt. Cook the artichokes for 10 minutes, or until just tender. Drain in a colander and dry on paper towels.

5. Heat the oil in a large skillet over medium heat.

6. Add the onions and cook, stirring, for 3 to 5 minutes, or until softened.

7. Add the artichokes and cook for 2 minutes.

8. Add the peas, asparagus, 3 tablespoons of water, and salt to taste. Simmer, stirring, for about 5 minutes, or until just cooked through.

9. Add the herbs and cook for 1 minute. Stir in the remaining 1 tablespoon of butter. Serve immediately.

Nutrition Information (per serving): 140 calories, 5 g protein, 13 g carbohydrates, 3 g fiber, 3 g sugar:, 7 g fat, 3 g saturated fat, 195 mg sodium

BEEF STEW WITH ROOT VEGETABLES

Prep Time: 30 minutes
Cook Time: 1 hour 45 minutes
Total Time: 2 hours 15 minutes

SERVINGS: 4

Beef stew is always super filling, and this version is no different. If you prefer to make it meat-free, here's how: Cut out the beef and skip step 1. Reduce the oil to 2 teaspoons and proceed with step 6, swapping the chicken broth for vegetable. Jump to step 4 and add 1½ cups of chopped sweet potatoes when you add the rutabaga.

1¼ pounds grass-fed beef chuck, cut into 1½" cubes

½ teaspoon salt

¼ teaspoon freshly ground black pepper

2 tablespoons extra-virgin olive oil, divided

½ large onion, chopped (about ¾ cup)

¼ teaspoon dried thyme

¼ teaspoon dried rosemary

2 cloves garlic, finely chopped

4 cups low-sodium chicken broth, divided

2 large parsnips, cut into 1" pieces (about 1½ cups)

3 medium carrots, cut into 1" pieces (about 1½ cups)

1 medium rutabaga, peeled and cut into 1" cubes (about 2 cups)

2 tablespoons red wine vinegar

2 tablespoons chopped, fresh flat-leaf parsley, for garnish (optional)

1. Season the beef with the salt and pepper.

2. Heat 1 tablespoon of the oil in a large pot or Dutch oven over medium-high heat. Add half of the beef, spacing the pieces at least ½" apart to avoid crowding. (If the pot isn't large enough to hold half of the beef without crowding, cook it in 3 batches.) Do not turn the beef for about 3 minutes, or until the bottoms of the cubes are browned. Turn and cook for about 2 minutes, or until the opposite sides are browned.

3. Transfer the beef to a bowl and repeat with the remaining 1 tablespoon of oil and beef.

4. Reduce the heat to medium and add the onion, thyme, and rosemary. Cook, stirring occasionally, for about 7 minutes, or until the onion is tender and lightly browned.

5. Add the garlic and cook, stirring, for about 1 minute. Add ¾ cup water and simmer for 3 to 4 minutes, or until the liquid is reduced by half.

6. Add 3 cups of the broth, cover, increase the heat to high, and bring to a boil. Add the beef and any juice that has accumulated in the bowl. Reduce the heat to medium-low and simmer, uncovered, stirring occasionally, for 30 minutes.

7. Add the parsnips and carrots. If necessary, add enough of the remaining broth to just cover the vegetables. Cover and simmer, stirring occasionally, for 20 minutes. Add the rutabaga, cover, and simmer, stirring occasionally, for about 20 minutes, or until all of the vegetables are tender and the beef is very tender. Stir in the vinegar. Season to taste with salt and pepper. Divide among 4 bowls and garnish with the parsley, if using.

Nutrition Information (per serving): 154 calories, 15 g protein, 11 g carbohydrates, 3 g fiber, 4 g sugar, 6 g fat, 2 g saturated fat, 211 mg sodium

CHILLED AVOCADO AND CUCUMBER SOUP

Prep Time: 10 minutes
Total Time: 4 hours 10 minutes

SERVINGS: 4

This make-ahead, warm-weather treat pairs well with a nice big salad to make a light and refreshing meal. Combining avocado with vegetables means that you'll get more bang for your buck, because healthy fats help you better absorb the nutrients found in root vegetables and greens.

2 unpeeled cucumbers

2 avocados, pitted and peeled

1 cup low-sodium vegetable broth

2 tablespoons chopped onion

1 tablespoon lemon juice

1 tablespoon chopped mint

1 teaspoon vinegar (we like to use rice wine vinegar)

½ teaspoon salt

¼ teaspoon freshly ground black pepper

1. In a blender, combine the cucumbers, avocados, broth, onion, lemon juice, mint, and vinegar.

2. Blend until smooth and then season with the salt and black pepper.

3. Chill for at least 4 hours, or even overnight.

Nutrition Information (per serving): 133 calories, 3 g protein, 9 g carbohydrates, 5 g fiber, 2 g sugar, 11 g fat, 1 g saturated fat, 932 mg sodium

CABBAGE AND BEEF SOUP

Prep Time: 15 minutes
Cook Time: 45 minutes
Total Time: 1 hour

SERVINGS: 8

When it comes to vitamin C, cabbage gives oranges a run for their money. This leafy green is an immunity-boosting powerhouse. Chow down on this nourishing soup when you feel a cold coming on; it'll put mom's chicken noodle to shame.

1 tablespoon extra-virgin olive oil	1 cup thinly sliced carrots
1 cup chopped onion	6 cups fat-free, low-sodium chicken broth
½ teaspoon thyme	½ teaspoon salt
8 ounces lean ground beef	½ teaspoon freshly ground black pepper
6 cups thinly sliced green cabbage	

1. Warm the oil in a large saucepan over medium heat. Add the onion and thyme.
2. Cook, stirring occasionally, for about 5 minutes, or until softened.
3. Add the beef. Cook, stirring occasionally, for about 4 minutes, or until the meat is no longer pink.
4. Add the cabbage, carrots, broth, salt, and pepper. Bring to a boil.
5. Reduce the heat and simmer for 30 minutes, or until the cabbage is very tender.

Nutrition Information (per serving): 79 calories, 7 g protein, 6 g carbohydrates, 2 g fiber, 2 g sugar, 3 g fat, 1 g saturated fat, 520 mg sodium

ROASTED BUTTERNUT, GARLIC, AND SAGE SOUP

Prep Time: 20 minutes
Cook Time: 1 hour 5 minutes
Total Time: 1 hour 25 minutes

SERVINGS: 10

The nutty, creamy flavor of this butternut squash soup gets its kick from garlic and onions, making this warm bowl of heaven a cold-weather classic. Plus, butternut squash is teeming with vitamin B_6, which is needed by your nervous and immune systems.

5 pounds (2 medium) butternut squash

2 medium onions, quartered

½ head garlic, separated into cloves (do not peel)

2 tablespoons extra-virgin olive oil

2 teaspoons coarse salt

½ teaspoon freshly ground black pepper

1 small bunch fresh sage (about 6 stems)

6 cups low-sodium chicken broth

2 teaspoons lemon juice

1. Position a rack in the middle of the oven and preheat it to 425°F.

2. Peel the squash, cut it in half, and remove and discard the seeds. Cut each half into 2 pieces.

3. Place the squash, onions, and garlic in a single layer in a large roasting pan. (Use 2 roasting pans or a large baking sheet, if necessary.) Drizzle the vegetables with the oil and toss to coat well, using your hands if necessary.

4. Sprinkle all the vegetables with the salt and pepper. Scatter three-fourths of the sage in the pan.

5. Roast for 1 hour, or until the squash is tender, turning the mixture after 30 minutes to avoid sticking. Remove from the oven and let cool.

6. Transfer the onions to a food processor. Squeeze the garlic cloves out of their skins and into the food processor. Add the squash and any liquid remaining in the roasting pan. Discard the sage. Process until pureed.

7. Transfer the puree to a soup pot and stir in the broth. Bring the soup to a simmer over high heat for 5 minutes. Remove from the heat, stir in the lemon juice, and serve.

Nutrition Information (per serving): 155 calories, 3 g protein, 32 g carbohydrates, 5 g fiber, 7 g sugar, 3 g fat, 0.5 g saturated fat, 560 mg sodium

ROOT VEGETABLE SOUP

Prep Time: 25 minutes
Cook Time: 1 hour 25 minutes
Total Time: 1 hour 50 minutes

SERVINGS: 6

Root vegetables are the forgotten vegetables, but there are plenty of reasons why you should incorporate them into your diet. These veggies are extremely high in fiber and are great sources of vitamins A and C. Parsnips are especially nutritious and can help lower high cholesterol levels.

1 tablespoon extra-virgin olive oil

6 cloves garlic, minced

2 large onions, chopped

½ teaspoon dried marjoram, crushed

½ teaspoon dried sage, crushed

¼ teaspoon salt

½ teaspoon freshly ground black pepper

1 pound lean, well-trimmed beef round, cut into 1" cubes

3 cups low-sodium beef broth

3 cups water

4 small turnips, peeled and cut into ½" chunks

3 medium beets, peeled and cut into ½" chunks

3 large carrots, cut into ½" chunks

2 medium parsnips, peeled and cut into ½" chunks

1. Heat the oil in a large saucepan over medium heat.

2. Add the garlic and onions and cook, stirring, for 5 minutes, or until soft. Add the marjoram, sage, salt, and pepper. Add the beef and cook, stirring, for 5 minutes, or until browned. Add the broth, and water.

3. Bring to a boil over high heat. Reduce the heat to low, cover, and simmer, stirring occasionally, for 45 minutes, or until the beef is very tender.

4. Add the turnips, beets, carrots, and parsnips. Return to a simmer.

5. Cover and cook, stirring occasionally, for 25 minutes, or until the vegetables are very tender, then serve.

Nutrition Information (per serving): 265 calories, 23 g protein, 28 g carbohydrates, 7 g fiber, 14 g sugar, 7 g fat, 2 g saturated fat, 283 mg sodium

CHILLED CARROT SOUP

Prep Time: 10 minutes
Cook Time: 50 minutes
Total Time: 4 hours, including chilling time

SERVINGS: 6

The natural sweetness of carrots and apples makes a wonderful chilled soup. To turn this into a zesty carrot soup, stir in 1 teaspoon of Dijon mustard and a sprinkle of black pepper while it's cooking.

3 cups cold water

2 cups apple juice

1 pound carrots, thinly sliced (2½ cups)

½ cup diced onion

½ cup brown rice

1 clove garlic, minced

½ teaspoon salt

1 tablespoon lemon juice

Minced fresh herbs (parsley, dill, chives, or chervil), for garnish

1. In a 3-quart saucepan, combine the water, juice, carrots, onion, rice, garlic, and salt.

2. Cover and bring to a boil. Reduce to a simmer and cook for about 45 minutes, or until the rice is tender.

3. In a blender or food processor, blend or process the mixture until smooth.

4. Place the puree in a bowl and stir in the lemon juice. Cover and chill for at least 3 hours or overnight. Garnish with the herbs and serve.

Nutrition Information (per serving): 135 calories, 2 g protein, 31 g carbohydrates, 3 g fiber, 12 g sugar, 1 g fat, 0 g saturated fat, 354 mg sodium

THAI SQUASH SOUP

Prep Time: 10 minutes
Cook Time: 20 minutes
Total Time: 30 minutes

SERVINGS: 6

Have fun with this *literally* all-natural dish: To make an edible bowl, cut a thin slice from the bottom of a small acorn squash. Cut off the top and scoop out the insides, leaving at least ½" of shell intact. Cook the bowl at 350°F for 35 to 40 minutes, or until tender when pricked with a fork. Fill the squash with delicious soup, then eat it when you've finished the soup!

6 shallots, unpeeled

1 can (13½ ounces) light coconut milk

2 cups low-sodium chicken broth

1½ pounds butternut squash, peeled and cut into ½" cubes

½ cup packed fresh cilantro + 1 tablespoon chopped, for garnish

½ teaspoon salt

2 tablespoons fish sauce

¼ cup minced scallions, green parts only

¼ teaspoon freshly ground black pepper

1. Preheat the broiler.

2. Coat a baking sheet with cooking spray and place the shallots on top. Broil the shallots, turning occasionally, for 5 to 7 minutes, or until they've softened and blackened.

3. Remove the shallots from the broiler, let them cool, and then peel and halve them lengthwise.

4. In a large pot over medium-high heat, combine the shallots, coconut milk, broth, squash, and ½ cup of the cilantro. Cook just until the mixture begins to boil.

5. Reduce the heat, add the salt, and simmer for about 10 minutes, or until the squash is tender.

6. Stir in the fish sauce and cook for 2 to 3 minutes.

7. Garnish each serving with a sprinkling of the minced scallion greens and the remaining 1 tablespoon of cilantro, then season with pepper to taste.

Nutrition Information (per serving): 161 calories, 7 g protein, 28 g carbohydrates, 2 g fiber, 6 g sugar, 4 g fat, 3 g saturated fat, 706 mg sodium

CARROT-GINGER SOUP

Prep Time: 20 minutes
Cook Time: 1 hour 5 minutes
Total Time: 1 hour 25 minutes

SERVINGS: 12

Enjoy this soup with a side of apple slices and celery for an antioxidant overload that your skin will thank you for. The combination of vitamin A in the carrots and vitamin C in the apples will leave your skin as smooth as a baby's.

---

4 tablespoons extra-virgin olive oil

2 cups finely chopped sweet onions

2 cloves garlic, minced

2 pounds carrots, finely diced

12 cups low-sodium vegetable stock

2 tablespoons minced fresh ginger

½ teaspoon salt + more to taste

½ teaspoon ground ginger

Freshly ground black pepper

½ cup homemade plain coconut yogurt (optional) (page 31)

1. Heat the oil over medium heat in a Dutch oven or a wide, heavy-bottomed pot large enough to hold all of the ingredients.

2. Add the onions and garlic and sauté for about 3 minutes, or until the onions are transparent. Add the carrots and cook uncovered, stirring, for about 5 minutes, or until slightly softened.

3. Add the stock, fresh ginger, salt, and ground ginger. Bring to a boil, lower the heat, stir, and simmer for about 45 minutes, or until the carrots are fork-tender.

4. Working in batches, move the soup to a blender and puree it until very smooth.

5. Return the soup to the pot and simmer gently over low heat until the soup is heated through. Season with the salt and pepper to taste. Stir and bring to a high simmer over medium heat.

6. Lower the heat, stir, and simmer gently for about 3 minutes, or until the soup is hot throughout. Do not let the bottom scorch. Swirl with coconut yogurt, if desired. The soup can be cooled, covered, and refrigerated for up to 2 days.

Nutrition Information (per serving): 105 calories, 1 g protein, 15 g carbohydrates, 3 g fiber, 7 g sugar, 5 g fat, 1 g saturated fat, 482 mg sodium

BALSAMIC BEETS

Prep Time: 15 minutes
Cook Time: 45 minutes
Total Time: 1 hour 30 minutes

SERVINGS: 4

This is the perfect dish to bring to a summer cookout, and it's easy to prepare. The beets and glaze in this recipe can be made up to 3 days in advance. Toss them together, chilled, right before serving for a cool salad.

1 pound beets (about 1 bunch), each about 2" in diameter, trimmed

¼ cup balsamic vinegar

1 medium bunch arugula (about 4 cups), trimmed and washed

1 tablespoon lemon juice

1 teaspoon grated lemon zest

1 tablespoon extra-virgin olive oil

¼ teaspoon salt

⅛ teaspoon freshly ground black pepper

1. Heat the oven to 425°F. Trim the beet stems and roots, leaving about 1" attached to the beets. Wrap the beets in foil and place them directly on the oven rack. Roast for 45 minutes, or until a knife easily pierces the beets. Cool for 30 minutes, then peel and cut each beet into 8 wedges and put them in a medium bowl.

2. Meanwhile, in a medium saucepan over medium-high heat, bring the vinegar to a boil and cook for 12 to 14 minutes, or until it's reduced to 2½ to 3 tablespoons of syrup. Toss the syrup with the beets.

3. In a large bowl, toss the arugula with the lemon juice, lemon zest, oil, salt, and pepper.

4. Arrange the arugula on 4 serving plates. Divide the beets into 4 portions and place each on top of the arugula. Drizzle any remaining balsamic syrup over each plate. Serve immediately.

Nutrition Information (per serving): 99 calories, 2 g protein, 15 g carbohydrates, 4 g fiber, 11 g sugar, 4 g fat, 0.5 g saturated fat, 243 mg sodium

ROASTED BEET AND BEET GREENS SAUTÉ

Prep Time: 20 minutes
Cook Time: 1 hour 14 minutes
Total Time: 1 hour 34 minutes

SERVINGS: 4

Studies show that beets can reduce blood pressure, eliminate inflammation, and avert oxidative stress. Incorporating beets into your diet could be your first step toward decreasing inflammation once and for all. If you prefer sweeter-tasting beets, look for dark red ones.

4 medium beets

1 tablespoon extra-virgin olive oil

2 cloves garlic, finely chopped

1 pound beet greens (about 2 bunches), stems trimmed, chopped

Salt

Freshly ground black pepper

1. Heat the oven to 425°F. Wrap the beets in foil and place them directly on the oven rack. Roast for 45 minutes, or until a knife easily pierces the beets.

2. When the beets are cool enough to handle, unwrap the foil. Trim the root and stem ends, slip the skins off, and chop up the beets. (You can do this up to 1 day ahead, then cover and refrigerate the chopped beets.)

3. Heat the oil in a large skillet over medium-low heat. Add the garlic and cook, stirring, for 1 minute. Increase the heat to medium, add the beet greens, toss well to coat with the garlic and oil, and cook for about 3 minutes, or until wilted.

4. Add enough water to thinly cover the bottom of the skillet (about ¼ cup) and bring it to a simmer. Cook, stirring frequently, for 3 to 4 minutes, or until the greens are tender and the liquid has evaporated.

5. Stir in the beets and cook for about 1 minute, or until heated through. Remove from the heat. Season to taste with the salt and pepper and serve.

Nutrition Information (per serving): 92 calories, 4 g protein, 13 g carbohydrates, 7 g fiber, 6 g sugar, 4 g fat, 0.5 g saturated fat, 320 mg sodium

THAI BEEF SALAD WITH MINT

Prep Time: 15 minutes
Cook Time: 10 minutes
Total Time: 25 minutes

SERVINGS: 4

You don't have to seek out an Asian market to make this crisp and flavorful salad—all of the ingredients are available at your local supermarket. Turn this dish into a delicious soup-and-salad combo with the Thai Squash Soup on page 47.

Beef

1 boneless beef strip steak (1½" thick), about 10 ounces

½ teaspoon kosher salt

½ teaspoon freshly ground black pepper

Dressing

2 tablespoons fresh lime juice

1 tablespoon fish sauce

Salad

1 small red onion, thinly sliced, rinsed, and drained

1 medium kirby cucumber, diced, cut into cubes

¼ cup fresh mint leaves, coarsely chopped

10 large basil leaves, thinly sliced

4 cups (about 2 hearts) romaine lettuce hearts sliced widthwise (small inner leaves can be left whole) or a variety of lettuces of your choice

1. *To make the beef:* Season the steak generously on both sides with the salt and pepper. Grill or pan-fry the steak (use a skillet that's been lightly coated with cooking spray) over medium-high heat for 4 to 5 minutes per side. (Steak is best rare to medium and still pink in the center.) Set the steak aside and keep it warm.

2. *To make the dressing:* In a large bowl, whisk together the lime juice and fish sauce. Remove 1 tablespoon and set it aside.

3. *To make the salad:* Add the onion, cucumber, mint, basil, and romaine to the large bowl and toss well with the dressing. Arrange the salad on a large platter.

4. Thinly slice the steak against the grain. In a small bowl, toss the steak with the reserved 1 tablespoon of dressing. Arrange the steak on top of the salad and serve immediately.

Nutrition Information (per serving): 191 calories, 6 g carbohydrates, 2 g fiber, 2 g sugar, 12 g fat, 5 g saturated fat, 636 mg sodium

BEEF SKEWERS WITH GRILLED VEGETABLES

Prep Time: 10 minutes
+ 1 to 8 hours marinade time
Cook Time: 17 minutes
Total Time: 27 minutes
+ marinade time

SERVINGS: 4

These skewers let you stretch an inexpensive top sirloin steak by slicing it into long, thin strips. They're an easy meal for one, two, or a dozen people. The longer you marinate the beef, the better the flavor will be. Let it sit overnight, if you have the time.

2 tablespoons + 2 teaspoons extra-virgin olive oil

2 tablespoons rice wine vinegar

1 tablespoon grated fresh ginger

2 cloves garlic, finely minced, plus 24 whole

½ teaspoon kosher salt

½ teaspoon freshly ground black pepper

1 pound top sirloin steak, preferably grass-fed, cut into 1" cubes

3 sprigs rosemary, cut into 6 pieces

4 scallions

1 medium zucchini, sliced into ¼" discs

1 medium summer squash, halved lengthwise

1. Place 2 tablespoons of the oil, the vinegar, ginger, minced garlic, salt, and pepper in a gallon-size resealable plastic bag or a large bowl. Seal and vigorously shake or whisk to combine. Add the steak strips, seal the bag or cover the bowl with plastic wrap, and refrigerate for at least 1 hour or overnight.

2. Soak eight 8-inch wooden skewers in warm water for 30 minutes.

3. Line a rimmed baking sheet with foil. With the remaining garlic, slice 8 cloves into thirds. Drain off the marinade and thread pieces of steak onto each skewer beginning and ending with a whole clove of garlic and rosemary and alternating with garlic slices between pieces of steak. Place the skewers on the baking sheet.

4. Heat a grill pan over high heat (or heat a grill to high). Using a silicone brush, coat the grill with the remaining 1 teaspoon of oil.

5. Grill the beef until it's browned on both sides, about 4 minutes total, working in batches, if necessary. (You'll probably have to cook the skewers in 3 or 4 batches unless you're cooking them on a big grill.) Use tongs to transfer them to a plate and let them rest for 5 minutes.

6. Brush the vegetables all over with the remaining teaspoon of oil and lay on the grill, cut side down. Cook until grill marks form on both sides and the vegetables are tender, about 5 minutes.

7. Serve the beef with the grilled scallions, zucchini, and squash.

Nutrition Information (per serving): 326 calories, 27 g protein, 11 g carbohydrates, 2 g fiber, 3 g sugar, 19 g fat, 5 g saturated fat, 316 mg sodium

COUNTRY COLESLAW

Prep Time: 15 minutes
Total Time: 3 hours

SERVINGS: 8

½ cup apple cider vinegar

⅓ cup organic, unsweetened apple juice

¼ cup honey

1 tablespoon extra-virgin olive oil

1 teaspoon celery seeds

1 head cabbage, thinly sliced (about 6 cups)

3 carrots, grated

1 bunch scallions, sliced

1 apple, grated

1. In a small saucepan, combine the vinegar, apple juice, honey, oil, and celery seeds. Cook, stirring, over medium-high heat for 2 to 3 minutes, or until the honey dissolves. Remove to cool.

2. Meanwhile, in a large bowl, combine the cabbage, carrots, scallions, and apple. Add the cooled dressing. Toss to coat.

3. Cover and chill, tossing occasionally, for 2 to 3 hours, or until well-chilled.

Nutrition Information (per serving): 96 calories, 1 g protein, 21 g carbohydrate, 3 g fiber, 15 g sugar, 2 g fat, 0 g saturated fat, 29 mg sodium

BRUSSELS SPROUTS SLAW WITH BEEF

Prep Time: 10 minutes
Cook Time: 12 minutes
Total Time: 45 minutes

SERVINGS: 1

Though it is on the pricier side, adding grass-fed beef to your diet can make a huge difference to your health. Grass-fed meat is higher in healthy unsaturated fats and lower in saturated fats than beef from conventionally raised cows, which eat corn-based feed that's supplemented with antibiotics and growth hormones.

⅛ teaspoon cinnamon

¼ teaspoon salt, plus more to taste

¼ teaspoon chili powder

½ teaspoon + 1 tablespoon extra-virgin olive oil

1 beef tenderloin (4 ounces)

3 tablespoons grapefruit juice

½ tablespoon scallion whites, minced

Freshly ground black pepper

1½ cups Brussels sprouts, shredded

¼ cup carrots, shredded

½ grapefruit, segmented

1½ tablespoons scallion greens, minced

1 tablespoon pomegranate seeds

1. Heat the oven to 400°F. In a small bowl, combine the cinnamon, salt, chili powder, and ½ teaspoon of the olive oil. Rub this mixture on the tenderloin.

2. In a small roasting pan, roast the beef for about 12 minutes, or until its internal temperature reaches 145°F for medium rare, or depending on how well-done you like it. Let it rest for 5 to 8 minutes.

3. In a medium bowl, whisk together the grapefruit juice, scallion whites, salt, pepper, and the remaining 1 tablespoon of olive oil. Toss with the Brussels sprouts, carrots, grapefruit segments, and scallion greens until coated. Sprinkle with the pomegranate seeds.

4. Slice the beef and serve it with the slaw.

Nutrition Information: 418 calories, 29 g protein, 24 g carbohydrates, 6 g fiber, 6 g sugar, 25 g fat, 6 g saturated fat, 852 mg sodium

SIMPLE BUFFALO BURGERS

Prep Time: 6 minutes
Cook Time: 16 minutes
Total Time: 22 minutes

SERVINGS: 4

Buffalo burgers are known for having less fat, fewer calories, and less cholesterol than traditional beef burgers, and they freeze just as well as beef burgers. Individually wrap each patty in plastic wrap and store them in a resealable freezer bag labeled with the date to avoid freezer burn.

1 pound lean ground buffalo

¼ cup finely chopped onion

1 tablespoon chopped fresh parsley

¼ teaspoon freshly ground black pepper

4 large iceberg lettuce leaves

1. Preheat the grill to medium.

2. In a large mixing bowl, combine the buffalo, onion, parsley, and pepper. Knead with your hands until thoroughly combined.

3. Form into 4 patties about ½" thick. (This will allow them to cook quickly.)

4. Grill the burgers for 8 minutes per side, or until a thermometer inserted in the centers registers 160°F and the meat is no longer pink.

5. Slide each burger onto a lettuce leaf and serve immediately.

Nutrition Information (per serving): 172 calories, 23 g protein, 2 g carbohydrates, 0 g fiber, 1 g sugar, 8 g fat, 3.5 g saturated fat, 82 mg sodium

STIR-FRIED CURLY KALE

Prep Time: 4 minutes
Cook Time: 7 minutes
Total Time: 11 minutes

SERVINGS: 4

Kale consistently tops nutritionists' lists of superfoods, and the nutritional benefits of kale are endless. High in antioxidants, this leafy green is one of the key players in the fight against chronic inflammation and oxidative stress.

---

1 tablespoon extra-virgin olive oil

2 teaspoons minced garlic

1 pound kale leaves, chopped or torn into small pieces

¼ teaspoon salt

Freshly ground black pepper

1. Heat the oil in a large skillet over low heat. Add the garlic and cook for about 3 minutes, or until the garlic is softened. Do not brown.

2. Increase the heat to high. Add half of the kale to the pan; toss with tongs. Cover for about 1 minute, or until the leaves start to wilt.

3. Add the remaining kale. Toss and cover for 1 minute. Uncover and cook, tossing, for about 2 minutes, or until the leaves are wilted, brightly colored, and glossy.

4. Add the salt and season with the pepper to taste. Toss to combine.

Nutrition Information (per serving): 68 calories, 3 g protein, 7 g carbohydrates, 1 g fiber, 0 g sugar, 4 g fat, 0.5 g saturated fat, 172 mg sodium

SPRING RICE BOWL WITH ASPARAGUS

Prep Time: 15 minutes
Cook Time: 35 minutes
Total Time: 50 minutes

SERVINGS: 4

Rice, which is technically a grass, contains an impressive range of nutrients, including phosphorus, zinc, magnesium, and B vitamins. Throw in some asparagus and you're fortifying your body with healthy levels of folate and vitamin B_{12}—both of which may help with cognitive impairment.

Rice

1 cup brown rice

Toppings

1 tablespoon extra-virgin olive oil

1 bunch asparagus, chopped

½ pound cremini mushrooms, sliced

Poached Eggs

¼ cup white vinegar

4 eggs

Dressing

3 tablespoons extra-virgin olive oil

Juice of ½ lemon

2 teaspoons chopped dill

1 clove garlic, minced

½ teaspoon salt

¼ teaspoon freshly ground black pepper

1. *To make the rice:* Prepare the rice according to the package directions.

2. *To make the toppings:* Warm the oil in a medium pan over medium heat. Add the asparagus and mushrooms, sautéing for 3 to 5 minutes, or until just tender.

3. *To poach the eggs:* Boil 8 inches of water in a large saucepan. Add the vinegar. Reduce the heat to a simmer. Stir gently. Crack eggs close to the surface of the water, taking care not to drop them on top of each other. Cook until whites are firm, but not hard, 3 to 5 minutes. Remove from the water with a slotted spoon.

4. *To make the dressing:* In a small bowl, whisk together the oil, lemon juice, dill, garlic, salt, and pepper.

5. Divide the rice among 4 bowls and top with the asparagus and an egg.

6. Drizzle the dressing over the rice mixture. Serve immediately.

Nutrition Information (per serving): 395 calories, 13 g protein, 42 g carbohydrates, 3 g fiber, 3 g sugar, 20 g fat, 4 g saturated fat, 446 mg sodium

ROASTED BUTTERNUT SQUASH SKEWERS WITH ROSEMARY DIP

Prep Time: 10 minutes
Cook Time: 35 minutes
Total Time: 45 minutes

SERVINGS: 4

Roasting butternut squash with a little bit of healthy fat, such as olive oil, will help you get the most nutrition out of its cancer-fighting antioxidants. Choose a heavy, firm, stem-on squash without soft spots, or buy the veggie peeled and cubed, to save time and effort.

2½ pounds butternut squash

1 tablespoon extra-virign olive oil, divided

¼ teaspoon salt

¼ teaspoon freshly ground black pepper, divided

½ cup homemade plain coconut yogurt (page 31)

½ teaspoon dried rosemary

1. Heat the oven to 425°F. Cut the squash in half lengthwise and scoop out the seeds. Peel and cut the squash halves into 1" to 1½" cubes. Place the cubes on a baking sheet, toss with 2 teaspoons of the oil, and sprinkle with the salt and ⅛ teaspoon of the pepper.

2. Roast the squash for 30 to 35 minutes, or until tender and lightly browned, stirring once or twice. Cool slightly.

3. Thread about 3 squash cubes onto each of 12 small wooden skewers.

4. In a small bowl, combine the yogurt, rosemary, the remaining 1 teaspoon of oil, and the remaining ⅛ teaspoon of the pepper. Serve alongside the skewers.

Nutrition Information (per serving): 202 calories, 3 g protein, 30 g carbohydrates, 5 g fiber, 6 g sugar, 10 g fat, 6 g saturated fat, 165 mg sodium

ALMOND-ENCRUSTED WILD SALMON WITH GREENS

Prep Time: 10 minutes
Cook Time: 7 minutes
Total Time: 17 minutes

SERVINGS: 2

For the cleanest cut of the pink fish, look for wild-caught salmon instead of farm-raised. Not only does wild salmon have half the fat and less sodium than farmed, but studies also show that farmed fish is higher in contaminants.

½ cup chopped soaked and sprouted almonds (available in the natural foods section of most grocery stores)

¼ cup chopped, fresh, flat-leaf parsley

1 tablespoon grated lemon zest

¼ teaspoon sea salt

Freshly ground black pepper

1 large egg

2 wild-caught skinless salmon fillets (6 to 8 ounces each)

2 tablespoons extra-virgin olive oil

4 cups mixed baby greens

Lemon wedges

1. In a wide, shallow bowl, combine the almonds, parsley, and lemon zest. Add the salt and pepper to taste. Mix well.

2. Beat the egg in another wide, shallow bowl.

3. Pat the salmon dry with a paper towel. Dip a salmon fillet in the egg, turning to coat. Transfer the fillet to the bowl with the almond mixture, turning, and press firmly so the almonds adhere. Set aside and repeat with the second fillet.

4. Warm the oil in a large skillet over medium heat. Add the salmon and cook for 5 to 7 minutes, or until it's opaque in the center, turning once.

5. Divide the greens between 2 plates and place a cooked salmon fillet on top of each. Garnish with the lemon wedges and serve immediately.

Nutrition information (per serving): 633 calories, 55 g protein, 10 g carbohydrates, 6 g fiber, 2 g sugar, 42 g fat, 6 g saturated fat, 365 mg sodium

BAKED SALMON

Prep Time: 5 minutes
Cook Time: 25 minutes
Total Time: 30 minutes

SERVINGS: 4

Make this dish ahead for quick meals. Store it in the refrigerator for up to 3 days. To reheat, arrange the fillets in a baking dish, cover, and bake at 350°F for 5 to 8 minutes, or until heated through. Or serve it cold over greens dressed with a mix of 1 part vinegar to 3 parts oil.

---

4 skinless, 1"-thick salmon fillets (6 ounces each)

1½ tablespoons lemon juice

½ teaspoon salt

¼ teaspoon freshly ground black pepper

1 teaspoon chopped fresh dill

1 teaspoon chopped chives

1. Preheat the oven to 375°F. Line a shallow baking dish that is large enough to fit the fillets in a single layer with parchment paper.

2. Arrange the salmon in the dish. Sprinkle with the lemon juice, salt, and pepper.

3. Fold together the ends of parchment to close. Bake for 20 to 24 minutes, or until the flesh is cooked through but still very juicy. Serve topped with the pan juices, dill, and chives.

Nutrition Information (per serving): 356 calories, 35 g protein, 1 g carbohydrates, 0 g fiber, 0 g sugar, 23 g fat, 5.5 g saturated fat, 391 mg sodium

CURRY-SPICED ROASTED CAULIFLOWER

Prep Time: 10 minutes
Cook Time: 35 minutes
Total Time: 45 minutes

SERVINGS: 2

Cauliflower, the cruciferous white veggie, is extremely versatile. It can act as a starchy substitute in dishes that call for potatoes, rice, and even flour, or it can stand in for meat in chicken and steak meals.

1 head cauliflower, cut into large pieces

1 tablespoon ground turmeric

1 tablespoon ground cumin

2 teaspoons ground ginger

1½ teaspoons ground coriander

½ teaspoon ground cinnamon

½ teaspoon sea salt + more to taste

2 tablespoons extra-virgin olive oil

2¼ cups cilantro leaves, finely chopped

1 tablespoon grated lime zest

1 teaspoon fresh lime juice

1. Preheat the oven to 320°F. Line a baking sheet with two 24"-long pieces of parchment paper. Set the papers perpendicular to one another to form a plus sign and set aside.

2. Keeping the cauliflower pieces intact, gently rub them with the turmeric, cumin, ginger, coriander, cinnamon, and ½ teaspoon of the salt.

3. Wrap the parchment around the cauliflower like you're wrapping a package: Fold the seams, tuck the ends under, and put it seam side down so no steam can escape.

4. Bake for about 35 minutes, or until the cauliflower is just tender.

5. Meanwhile, in a small bowl, combine the oil, cilantro, lime zest, 1 teaspoon of the lime juice, and salt to taste.

6. When the cauliflower is tender, carefully open the package, transfer it to a plate, top it with the dressing, and serve.

Nutrition Information (per serving): 237 calories, 7 g protein, 21 g carbohydrates, 9 g fiber, 6 g sugar, 16 g fat, 2 g saturated fat, 242 mg sodium

CHICKEN STIR-FRY

Prep Time: 5 minutes
Cook Time: 6 minutes
Total Time: 11 minutes

SERVINGS: 1

A stir-fry is a fast way to combine your favorite foods in one dish. Cut the chicken and vegetables into bite-size pieces before you start cooking. If you'd like, throw in extra veggies for added flavor and a healthy way to fill up fast.

1 tablespoon extra-virgin olive oil

8 ounces ground chicken

⅓ cup asparagus tips

⅓ cup broccoli

⅓ cup thinly sliced carrots

¼ medium red onion, cut into bite-size pieces

⅓ cup fresh or frozen green beans

½ cup cooked organic brown rice (optional)

1. Heat the oil in a skillet over high heat. Add the chicken and cook for 2 to 3 minutes, stirring frequently.

2. Add the asparagus, broccoli, carrots, onion, and green beans to the skillet and cook for 2 to 3 minutes, stirring frequently.

3. Serve over brown rice, if desired.

Nutrition Information [without rice]: 368 calories, 29 g protein, 14 g carbohydrates, 5 g fiber, 5 g sugar, 22 g fat, 3 g saturated fat, 171 mg sodium

Nutrition Information [with ½ cup cooked brown rice]: 477 calories, 32 g protein, 37 g carbohydrates, 7 g fiber, 5 g sugar, 23 g fat, 3 g saturated fat, 172 mg sodium

LAMB LOLLIPOPS (page 81)

DINNER

Healthy Endings

PLANK SALMON WITH GREEN BEANS

Prep Time: 2 hours 13 minutes
Cook Time: 12 minutes
Total Time: 2 hours 25 minutes

SERVINGS: 2

There is something special about grilling fish on a plank. But don't worry if you don't have a grill—you can always put the plank in the oven. Preheat it for 10 to 15 minutes at 350°F, add the fish, and bake for about 35 minutes, depending on the thickness of the fish, or until the flesh is opaque.

1 large, untreated cedar plank

2 tablespoons rice wine vinegar

2 tablespoons chopped fresh mint or cilantro

½ teaspoon salt + more to taste

¼ teaspoon freshly ground black pepper + more to taste

2 salmon fillets (6 ounces each)

½ cup halved green beans

1. Soak the cedar plank in water for at least 2 hours.

2. In a medium bowl, combine the vinegar and mint or cilantro. Season with the ½ teaspoon salt and ¼ teaspoon black pepper.

3. Preheat the grill to high. Lay the cedar plank on the grill.

4. Season the salmon with salt and pepper to taste.

5. When the plank begins to smoke, lay the fillets on it, skin side down. Close the top and grill for 10 to 12 minutes, or until the salmon flakes with light pressure from your finger.

6. Meanwhile, place a steamer basket in a large pot with 1" of water. Bring to a boil over high heat. Steam the beans in the basket for 3 to 5 minutes, or until they're bright green.

7. Serve immediately with green beans.

Nutrition Information (per serving): 382 calories, 37 g protein, 6 g carbohydrates, 3 g fiber, 3 g sugar, 23 g fat, 5 g saturated fat, 682 mg sodium

SALMON WITH AVOCADO SALSA

Prep Time: 15 minutes
Cook Time: 10 minutes
Total Time: 1 hour

SERVINGS: 2

With its impressive amount of brain-boosting omega-3s, plus loads of protein, vitamin D, and B vitamins, salmon is a great catch. Topped with avocado (another source of healthy fat), you have a cholesterol-fighting meal that tastes heavenly.

1 avocado, peeled, pitted, and chopped

1 small red onion, chopped

¼ cup chopped fresh cilantro

3 tablespoons freshly squeezed lime juice

1 clove garlic, minced

¼ teaspoon salt

¼ teaspoon freshly ground black pepper

1 tablespoon extra-virgin olive oil

2 wild salmon fillets (6 ounces each)

1. In a small bowl, combine the avocado, onion, cilantro, lime juice, garlic, salt and pepper.

2. Cover and let the mixture stand for at least 30 minutes to blend the flavors.

3. Heat the oil in a large nonstick skillet over medium-high heat. Sear the fillets for 10 minutes, turning once, or until opaque.

4. Divide the salmon between 2 plates. Serve with the salsa.

Nutrition Information (per serving): 446 calories, 39 g protein, 12 g carbohydrates, 6 g fiber, 2 g sugar, 27 g fat, 4.5 g saturated fat, 379 mg sodium

POACHED SALMON WITH VEGETABLES

Prep Time: 10 minutes
Cook Time: 18 minutes
Total Time: 28 minutes

SERVINGS: 1

When choosing vegetables, consider zucchini and snap peas, which pair well with full-flavored fish. Buy thick fillets, which will cook for as long as the veggies without drying out. Test fillets for freshness by pressing with your finger—the flesh should spring back, leaving no indentation.

1 skin-on salmon fillet (6 ounces)

1 celery stalk, diced

Pinch of lemon pepper

1½ cups raw vegetables, such as zucchini, snap peas, carrots, snow peas, and asparagus, cut into bite-size pieces

1. In a medium pot, combine the salmon, celery, and lemon pepper with just enough water to cover the fish completely. (Don't fill the pot more than you have to.) Bring the water to a slow boil over medium-high heat and cook for about 10 minutes, or until the thickest part of the fish is firm and cooked through.

2. Using a spatula, remove the salmon to a plate, gently turn it over, and scrape the skin from the underside. Discard the celery.

3. Meanwhile, place a steamer basket in a large pot with 1" of water. Bring to a boil over high heat. Steam the mixed vegetables in the basket for 3 to 5 minutes, or until they are tender yet bright. Serve with the salmon immediately.

Nutrition Information: 406 calories, 38 g protein, 11 g carbohydrates, 4 g fiber, 6 g sugar, 23 g fat, 5 g saturated fat, 147 mg sodium

MARINATED BROILED COD

Prep Time: 5 minutes
Cook Time: 7 minutes
Total Time: 1 hour 12 minutes

SERVINGS: 4

Whitefish like cod are bursting with heart-healthy nutrients. They are good sources of omega-3 fatty acids and are high in vitamin B_{12}. Scrod refers to a young whitefish, such as cod or haddock, and is generally not quite as thick as cod. Either would work in this preparation, as would grouper or tilapia.

½ cup apple cider vinegar

2 tablespoons extra-virgin olive oil

4 cloves garlic, minced

1 teaspoon dried thyme

2 pounds thick cod fillets

1. In a baking dish, whisk together the vinegar, oil, garlic, and thyme. Reserve 2 tablespoons of marinade.

2. Add the fillets, turning to coat. Cover and marinate in the refrigerator for 1 hour.

3. Preheat the broiler. Lift the cod from the marinade and place on a broiler pan.

4. Broil 4" from the heat, basting once with the reserved marinade, for 7 minutes, or until the fish just flakes when tested with a fork. Serve immediately.

Nutrition Information (per serving): 194 calories, 40 g protein, 1 g carbohydrates, 0 g fiber, 0 g sugar, 2 g fat, 1 g saturated fat, 123 mg sodium

LEMON CAPER HALIBUT

Prep Time: 12 minutes
Cook Time: 13 minutes
Total Time: 25 minutes

SERVINGS: 6

Adding citrus juice to fish is a great way to build flavor without adding significant calories. The acidity of lemon juice brings out the natural flavor of the fish, so you don't need to add extra oil.

1½ pounds halibut fillets

¼ teaspoon sea salt + more to taste

¼ teaspoon freshly ground black pepper + more to taste

5 tablespoons extra-virgin olive oil, divided

¼ cup nonpareil capers, rinsed and drained

2 tablespoons chopped shallots

1 teaspoon finely grated lemon zest

3 tablespoons lemon juice

1 tablespoon chopped flat-leaf parsley

1. Season the halibut on both sides with the salt and pepper.

2. In a 12" nonstick skillet, heat 2 tablespoons of the oil over medium-high heat. Place half of the fish in the skillet. Cook, turning once, for 2 to 3 minutes, or until the fish just flakes when tested with a fork and the edges are golden brown.

3. Transfer to a warm platter. Add 1 tablespoon of the oil to the skillet, if necessary, and cook the remaining fish as you did in step 2.

4. After the fish is cooked, add the capers, shallots, and remaining 2 tablespoons of oil to the skillet. Cook for about 1 minute, or until the shallots are golden. Add the lemon zest and juice and bring to a boil. Reduce the heat and simmer for 1 minute.

5. Add salt and pepper to taste.

6. Remove from the heat. Pour the sauce over the fish, garnish with the parsley, and serve immediately.

Nutrition Information (per serving): 278 calories, 24 g protein, 2 g carbohydrates, 0 g fiber, 0 g sugar, 19 g fat, 7 g saturated fat, 313 mg sodium

TROUT WITH CABBAGE

Prep Time: 15 minutes
Cook Time: 30 minutes
Total Time: 45 minutes

SERVINGS: 2

If you don't want your kitchen to smell fishy, start by buying the freshest fish you can find—that is, one that's been minimally exposed to air. Fish contain a chemical called trimethylamine oxide that breaks down once they've been exposed, so the fresher the fish, the less you'll smell the ammonia-like stench. The next step is to make sure you turn on your exhaust fan or open a window while cooking.

6 cups ½"-thick strips savoy cabbage

2 sprigs fresh thyme + 2 teaspoons thyme leaves

¼ cup water

1 tablespoon apple cider vinegar

3 teaspoons extra-virgin olive oil, divided

Coarse sea salt

2 wild trout (8 to 9 ounces each), cleaned and butterflied by fishmonger

½ scallion, diced (optional)

6 lemon slices (⅛" thick) + juice to taste for serving

1. Preheat the oven to 325°F.

2. In a large pot, combine the cabbage, thyme sprigs, and water. Cover and cook over medium-low heat, stirring occasionally, for 8 to 10 minutes, or until tender. Stir in the vinegar and 1 teaspoon of the oil.

3. Remove the thyme and season the cabbage with salt to taste. Transfer the cabbage to a bowl and set it aside in a warm place.

4. Place both fish, open, on a cutting board. Top each with 1 teaspoon of the thyme leaves and the diced scallion (if using).

5. Place 3 lemon slices on each fish and close the trout. Tie with string, as shown. Rub the fish with the remaining olive oil, transfer it to an ovenproof skillet, cover, and bake for 18 to 20 minutes, or until just firm and opaque. Season to taste with lemon juice.

Nutrition Information (per serving): 387 calories, 28 g protein, 14 g carbohydrates, 7 g fiber, 5 g sugar, 25 g fat, 12 g saturated fat, 220 mg sodium

PAN-FRIED RED SNAPPER

Prep Time: 20 minutes
Cook Time: 6 minutes
Total Time: 26 minutes

SERVINGS: 4

Whitefish is the ultimate dinner. It's healthy, quick to cook, and can be used fresh or frozen. Almost any firm, white-fleshed fish can be used in this recipe if you can't find snapper. Try grouper, sea bass, redfish (red drum), or pompano as a replacement.

½ teaspoon dried oregano, crushed

¼ teaspoon garlic powder

¼ teaspoon onion powder

¼ teaspoon salt

¼ teaspoon freshly ground black pepper

4 red snapper fillets (5 ounces each)

2 teaspoons extra-virgin olive oil

1. In a small bowl, combine the oregano, garlic powder, onion powder, salt, and pepper.

2. Coat a large cast-iron skillet with cooking spray and place it over high heat.

3. Brush both sides of the snapper with the oil and rub it with the spice mixture. Place the fish in the skillet and cook, turning once, for 6 minutes, or until the fish flakes easily. Serve immediately.

Nutrition Information (per serving): 164 calories, 29 g protein, 0 g carbohydrates, 0 g fiber, 0 g sugar, 4 g fat, 0.5 g saturated fat, 236 mg sodium

LAMB LOLLIPOPS

Prep Time: 5 minutes
Cook Time: 10 minutes
Total Time: 15 minutes

SERVINGS: 4

It's been said that we eat first with our eyes, so have fun with this dish and get creative with its presentation. Take advantage of the built-in "stick" and turn this chop into lollipops for grown-ups. Top these succulent meat pops with a dab of coconut yogurt for added flavor and a tasty garnish.

1 cup homemade plain coconut yogurt (page 31)

1 tablespoon lemon juice

⅛ teaspoon ground cumin

8 rib lamb chops

½ teaspoon freshly ground black pepper

Chopped mint (optional)

1. Preheat the grill to medium and coat the grates with cooking spray.

2. In a small bowl, combine the yogurt, lemon juice, and cumin. Mix well and refrigerate until needed.

3. Sprinkle both sides of the lamb chops with the pepper.

4. Grill for 5 minutes per side, or until cooked through.

5. Serve with the yogurt sauce and the mint, if desired.

Nutrition Information (per serving): 541 calories, 25 g protein, 4 g carbohydrates, 0 g fiber, 2 g sugar, 46 g fat, 28 g saturated fat, 115 mg sodium

HERB-MARINATED LAMB CHOPS

Prep Time: 10 minutes
Cook Time: 17 minutes
Total Time: 1 hours 52 minutes

SERVINGS: 8

Lamb is an excellent source of protein, and its nutritional strength is doubled when you add rosemary to the recipe. This minty herb is known for aiding digestion, enhancing memory, and boosting immunity.

Lamb Chops

- 8 sprigs fresh thyme, lightly pounded
- 8 large sprigs fresh rosemary, lightly pounded
- 8 large cloves garlic, smashed and peeled
- 3 tablespoons extra-virgin olive oil
- 2 teaspoons crushed peppercorns
- 8 double-cut rib lamb chops
- 1 teaspoon sea salt

Tapenade

- ½ cup pitted kalamata olives, rinsed and drained
- 5 anchovy fillets
- 1 teaspoon minced shallot
- 2 cloves garlic, chopped
- 2 tablespoons extra-virgin olive oil

1. *To make the lamb chops:* In a large glass baking dish, combine the thyme, rosemary, garlic, oil, and peppercorns. Add the lamb chops and toss to coat. Cover and marinate in the refrigerator for at least 1 hour 30 minutes or as long as overnight. Remove the chops from the refrigerator 30 minutes before cooking.

2. Preheat the oven to 400°F. Scrape the marinade off the chops and sprinkle them with the salt. Heat a 12" ovenproof skillet over medium-high heat. Sear the chops on both sides, about 3 minutes each. (Cook in batches of 4, transferring the chops to a warm plate when they're done.) Return the chops to the skillet and arrange them on their edges, fat side down, with the bones facing up.

3. Transfer the skillet to the oven and roast for 5 to 8 minutes, until a meat thermometer registers about 130°F for medium-rare. Transfer the chops to a cutting board and cover them loosely with foil. Let the chops rest for 8 minutes.

4. *To make the tapenade:* In a food processor, combine the olives, anchovies, shallot, garlic, and oil. Process until it reaches the desired consistency.

5. Slice the chops between the bones and serve with dollops of the tapenade.

Nutrition Information (per serving): 98 calories, 14 g protein, 0 g carbohydrates, 0 g fiber, 0 g sugar, 4 g fat, 1.5 g saturated fat, 64 mg sodium

LAMB AND ASPARAGUS

Prep Time: 5 minutes
Cook Time: 11 minutes
Total Time: 16 minutes

SERVINGS: 4

Before cooking the lamb chops, cut off the fat. If the chops are thick, pound them a little with the flat side of a chef's knife or the flat side of a meat mallet so that they cook more evenly.

½ cup extra-virgin olive oil, divided

1 small clove garlic, minced

⅜ teaspoon freshly ground black pepper

4 thick shoulder lamb chops, about 10 ounces each

4 teaspoons ground cumin

½ teaspoon salt + more to taste

2 cups steamed asparagus

2 cups wild arugula (loosely packed)

2 tablespoons freshly squeezed lemon juice

1. Heat the broiler to high.

2. In a small bowl, combine the ¼ cup of the oil, the garlic, and ⅛ teaspoon of pepper.

3. Season the chops with the cumin, salt, and ¼ teaspoon of pepper.

4. Place the chops on a broiler pan; broil for 3 minutes on each side, until cooked to desired doneness. Remove from the oven and let rest for 5 minutes.

5. Meanwhile, set 1-inch of water to boil in a 3-quart saucepan and cover. Insert steamer basket with asparagus and steam until bright green and tender, about 5 minutes.

6. Put the arugula in a large bowl. Drizzle with the remaining ¼ cup of the oil and the lemon juice. Add salt and pepper to taste.

7. Arrange the arugula evenly on 4 plates. Top each with a lamb chop and serve with the asparagus.

Nutrition Information (per serving): 493 calories, 37 g protein, 3 g carbohydrates, 1 g fiber, 1 g sugar, 37 g fat, 7 g saturated fat, 577 mg sodium

BROILED LAMB CHOPS WITH SPINACH

Prep Time: 10 minutes
Cook Time: 20 minutes
Total Time: 30 minutes

SERVINGS: 4

Rosemary and spinach have a fresh, light flavor that plays nicely off the hearty taste of the lamb. Plus, spinach is rich in vitamin K, which has been shown to strengthen bone density—good for fighting osteoporosis.

1 tablespoon extra-virgin olive oil

1 large onion, thinly sliced

¼ teaspoon honey

1 teaspoon chopped fresh rosemary

3 cloves garlic, sliced

¾ cup low-sodium beef broth

6 cups baby spinach

¼ teaspoon + ⅛ teaspoon salt

¼ teaspoon freshly ground black pepper, divided

4 loin lamb chops (3 to 4 ounces each), trimmed of all visible fat

1. Preheat the broiler. Coat a broiler pan with cooking spray.

2. Heat the oil in a large nonstick skillet over medium-high heat. Add the onion, honey, and rosemary and cook for 7 minutes, stirring occasionally, or until the rosemary starts to brown.

3. Add the garlic and cook for 2 minutes. Stir in the broth, bring to a boil, and cook for 1 minute.

4. Add the spinach and cook, stirring, for 1 minute, or until wilted.

5. Remove from the heat and stir in ¼ teaspoon of the salt and ⅛ teaspoon of the pepper.

6. Sprinkle the lamb chops with the remaining ⅛ teaspoon of salt and ⅛ teaspoon of pepper. Place the chops on the broiler pan and broil 4" from the heat for 6 minutes, turning once, or until browned and a thermometer inserted in the center registers 145°F for medium-rare.

7. Serve immediately.

Nutrition Information (per serving): 282 calories, 24 g protein, 13 g carbohydrates, 6 g fiber, 3 g sugar, 9 g fat, 2.5 g saturated fat, 530 mg sodium

GRILLED ROSEMARY-LEMON TURKEY

Prep Time: 12 minutes +
marinating time
Cook Time: 10 minutes
Total Time: 1 hour 20 minutes

SERVINGS: 4

2 tablespoons chopped fresh rosemary
leaves

1½ teaspoons grated lemon zest

2 tablespoons lemon juice

1 tablespoon extra-virgin olive oil

½ teaspoon freshly ground black pepper

¼ teaspoon salt

2 cloves garlic, peeled and smashed

1 pound turkey cutlets (4 ounces each)

Lemon wedges (optional)

1. In a pie plate, mix 1½ tablespoons of the rosemary, the lemon zest, lemon juice, oil, pepper, and salt. Add the garlic and turkey cutlets and turn to coat with the marinade. Cover and marinate in the refrigerator for 1 to 2 hours.

2. Heat a grill to medium heat. Turn the turkey once more in the marinade and place on the grill. Cover and grill, turning once, for 2 to 4 minutes per side, until just cooked through.

3. Sprinkle the turkey cutlets with the remaining ½ tablespoon of the rosemary, and serve with lemon wedges.

Nutrition Information (per serving): 158 calories, 28 g protein, 2 g carbohydrates, 0.5g fiber, 0.5 g sugar, 4 g fat, 0.5 g saturated fat, 246 mg sodium

SAGE TURKEY CUTLETS WITH SQUASH

Prep Time: 4 minutes
Cook Time: 25 minutes
Total Time: 30 minutes

SERVINGS: 4

2 pounds peeled, precut butternut squash, chopped into ¾" chunks

4 thin turkey cutlets (4–6 ounces each), halved

½ teaspoon salt

Freshly ground black pepper, to taste

8 whole fresh sage leaves

1 tablespoon extra-virgin olive oil

⅓ cup balsamic vinegar

1. Steam squash until tender when pierced with fork, about 10 minutes.

2. Season cutlets with ¼ teaspoon of the salt and the pepper, to taste. Press a sage leaf into center of each.

3. Heat 1½ teaspoons of the oil in skillet over medium high heat. Add 4 cutlets, leaf side down. Cook 1 to 1½ minutes, until edges whiten. Flip and cook through. Repeat with remaining oil and cutlets. Set aside.

4. Pour vinegar into skillet. Cook until reduced by half, about 2 minutes. Place squash in medium bowl, mash with fork, and season with remaining salt and pepper, to taste. To serve, divide squash among 4 plates and top with 2 cutlet pieces and a drizzle of balsamic sauce. Serve with green salad, if desired.

Nutrition Information (per serving): 273 calories, 30 g protein, 31 g carbohydrates, 5 g fiber, 8 g sugar, 4 g fat, 1 g saturated fat, 405 mg sodium

ONE-DISH TURKEY SUPPER

Prep Time: 20 minutes
Cook Time: 45 minutes
Total Time: 1 hour 5 minutes

SERVINGS: 6

This dish includes sweet potatoes, which are known to be one of the healthiest foods. They contain antioxidants that can enhance nutrient metabolism and immune system health as well as counter the effects of secondhand smoke and prevent diabetes.

1½ pounds turkey breast cutlets

1½ teaspoons dried thyme, divided

½ teaspoon freshly ground black pepper, divided

2 teaspoons extra-virgin olive oil

1 large onion, chopped

1 large clove garlic, minced

2¾ cups defatted chicken broth, divided

1¼ cups organic brown rice

1 small sweet potato, peeled and chopped

1 cup chopped yellow summer squash

¼ cup chopped fresh parsley

1 large bay leaf

1 teaspoon dried sage

¼ teaspoon salt (optional)

1. Sprinkle the turkey with ½ teaspoon of the thyme and ¼ teaspoon of the pepper. Coat a large nonstick skillet with cooking spray and place it over medium heat. Add the turkey, browning the pieces for 1 minute on each side. Remove and set aside.

2. In the same skillet, warm the oil over medium heat. Add the onion, garlic, and 3 tablespoons of the broth. Cook over medium heat, stirring, for 5 minutes, or until the onions are tender.

3. Stir in the rice, sweet potato, squash, parsley, bay leaf, sage, salt (if using), and the remaining 1 teaspoon of thyme, ¼ teaspoon of pepper, and broth. Bring to a boil. Reduce the heat to low, cover, and simmer for 12 minutes.

4. Place the turkey on top of the rice mixture. Cover and simmer for 25 minutes, or until the rice is tender and the liquid is absorbed. Remove and discard the bay leaf. Move the turkey to one side of the skillet.

5. Stir the rice, then transfer it to a serving platter. Arrange the turkey on top and serve.

Nutrition Information (per serving): 315 calories, 35 g protein, 36 g carbohydrates, 2 g fiber, 2 g sugar, 3 g fat, 0.5 g saturated fat, 287 mg sodium

GARLIC CHICKEN AND SPINACH

Prep Time: 10 minutes
Cook Time: 16 minutes
Total Time: 26 minutes

SERVINGS: 4

Garlic powder is convenient, but nothing beats the real deal. Raw garlic is a bulb exploding with vitamins, minerals, and amino acids. Avoid anything canned or jarred: Raw bulbs are best. Chopping garlic exposes it to air and releases allicin, a healthy compound with antibacterial properties.

8 ounces sliced mushrooms

1 teaspoon extra-virgin olive oil

1 pound boneless, skinless chicken breasts, cut into strips

4 large cloves garlic, minced

2 tablespoons water

2 tablespoons fresh lemon juice

½ teaspoon freshly ground black pepper

10 ounces frozen leaf spinach, steamed according to package instructions and drained

1. Coat a large, deep, heavy skillet with cooking spray and place it over medium heat. Add the mushrooms. Cook, stirring occasionally, for 6 minutes, or until they've released their juices. Transfer the mushrooms to a plate.

2. Heat the oil in the same skillet over medium heat. Add the chicken and garlic. Cook for 6 minutes, or until the chicken is cooked through, stirring occasionally.

3. Add the water, lemon juice, and pepper to the skillet. Cook for 1 minute, stirring, or until the pan juices are bubbling and thickened.

4. Return the mushrooms to the pan and cook for 3 minutes, stirring, or until heated through. Serve the chicken and mushrooms with the cooked spinach.

Nutrition Information (per serving): 180 calories, 29 g protein, 7 g carbohydrates, 3 g fiber, 2 g sugar, 5 g fat, 1 g saturated fat, 188 mg sodium

TUSCAN COUNTRY CHICKEN

Prep Time: 10 minutes
Cook Time: 1 hour 25 minutes
Total Time: 1 hour 35 minutes

SERVINGS: 4

Fresh bay leaves, better known for crowning Greek gods than for cooking, are used to amp up the flavor of this chicken. These leaves are an underrated flavor enhancer overflowing with nutritional benefits. Packed with antioxidants, bay leaves have been shown to help treat diabetes and enhance heart health.

1 chicken (3½ to 4 pounds)
Salt
Freshly ground black pepper
12 fresh or 6 dried bay leaves

1 lemon, quartered, plus extra wedges for garnish
2 cloves garlic, halved

1. Preheat the oven to 400°F. Place a rack in a roasting pan.

2. Pat the chicken dry with paper towels. Season it inside and out with salt and pepper to taste. With your fingers, loosen the skin over the chicken breast and slip 11 fresh or 5 dried bay leaves under the skin. In the cavity, place the lemon quarters, garlic, and remaining bay leaf. Secure the cavity with toothpicks or a wooden skewer.

3. Place the chicken on the rack in the pan. Roast for 1 hour and 15 minutes to 1 hour and 30 minutes, or until the chicken is well browned, a thermometer inserted in the thigh (not touching bone) registers 165°F, and the juices run clear.

4. Transfer the chicken to a serving platter and let it stand for 10 minutes. Discard the bay leaves. Carve the chicken, remove the skin, and serve with lemon wedges for garnish, if desired.

Nutrition Information (per serving): 441 calories, 82 g protein, 0 g carbohydrates, 0 g fiber, 0 g sugar, 11 g fat, 2.5 g saturated fat, 443 mg sodium

ROASTED CHICKEN BREASTS WITH SAUTÉED CABBAGE AND APPLES

Prep Time: 10 minutes
Cook Time: 35 minutes
Total Time: 1 hour

SERVINGS: 4

Want great-tasting cabbage? Don't overcook it. Raw cabbage has a mild flavor and adds color and crunch to slaws. A quick sauté makes it pleasantly pungent, but if you go too far, the sulfur compounds take over.

---

2 tablespoons chopped fresh sage

½ teaspoon salt + more to taste

¼ teaspoon freshly ground black pepper + more to taste

1¼ teaspoons dried thyme, divided

4 split bone-in chicken breasts (about 12 ounces each)

1 tablespoon extra-virgin olive oil

½ cup chopped onion

½ large red cabbage, cored and sliced (about 5 cups)

1 tablespoon honey

1 large Granny Smith apple, cored and thinly sliced

1. Heat the oven to 400°F. Coat a baking sheet with cooking spray. Combine the chopped sage, ½ teaspoon salt, ¼ teaspoon pepper, and 1 teaspoon of the thyme in a small bowl. Rub one-third of the herb mixture evenly on the bottom sides (not the skin side) of the chicken breasts. Turn them skin side up. Gently lift the skin and use your fingers to slide the remaining seasoning between the skin and the flesh. Place the breasts on the prepared baking sheet and roast for 35 to 40 minutes, or until cooked through.

2. Meanwhile, heat the oil in a large skillet over medium heat. Add the onion and the remaining ¼ teaspoon thyme and cook, stirring occasionally, for 4 to 5 minutes, or until the onion is lightly browned. Raise the heat to medium-high. Add the cabbage and cook, tossing constantly with tongs or a spatula, for about 2 minutes, or until just wilted. Add the honey and cook, stirring frequently, for 4 to 5 minutes, or until the liquid is nearly evaporated and the cabbage is crisp-tender. Add the apple and cook until just softened, about 2 minutes. Season to taste with salt and pepper.

3. Divide the chicken and the cabbage mixture among 4 plates and serve.

Nutrition Information (per serving): 503 calories, 61 g protein, 21 g carbohydrates, 4 g fiber, 14 g sugar, 19 g fat, 5 g saturated fat, 457 mg sodium

ITALIAN CHICKEN AND VEGETABLES

Prep Time: 10 minutes
Cook Time: 25 minutes
Total Time: 35 minutes

SERVINGS: 4

The notion that you need pasta for a decadent Italian meal is overrated. Using an Italian spice blend, you'll feel as if you're drinking Chianti in the countryside, even if you are just in your kitchen. *Buon appetito!*

---

1 tablespoon vegetable oil

1 pound small boneless, skinless chicken breasts

2 medium sweet potatoes, peeled and cubed

3 tablespoons water, divided

2 small zucchini, sliced

2 small yellow squash, sliced

1 cup asparagus tips, cut into 1" pieces

1½ teaspoons dried Italian seasoning

1. Warm the oil in a large skillet over medium-high heat. When hot, add the chicken and cook for about 5 minutes per side, or until brown. Reduce the heat and add the sweet potatoes and 2 tablespoons of the water. Cover and simmer for 10 minutes.

2. Add the zucchini, squash, and asparagus, then sprinkle with the Italian seasoning. Add the remaining 1 tablespoon of water, cover, and cook for 5 minutes, or until the vegetables are fork-tender. Serve immediately.

Nutrition Information (per serving): 244 calories, 27 g protein, 19 g carbohydrates, 4 g fiber, 7 g sugar, 6 g fat, 1 g saturated fat, 285 mg sodium

HERB-ROASTED CHICKEN WITH ROASTED VEGETABLES

Prep Time: 10 minutes
Cook Time: 50 minutes
Total Time: 1 hour + salting time

SERVINGS: 6

Flu got you down? Fight it off fast by adding thyme to your chicken, like in this herb-roasted recipe. Thyme has long been known to be an expectorant, so it makes coughs more productive. That clears out your lungs faster so you feel better, sooner.

1¼ teaspoons salt, divided

1 fryer chicken (3 to 4 pounds)

1 tablespoon extra-virgin olive oil, divided

3 tablespoons chopped fresh tarragon, thyme, or rosemary, or a mix, divided

½ head cauliflower, broken into florets

1 crown broccoli, broken into florets

¼ teaspoon freshly ground black pepper

1. Using 1 teaspoon of the salt, salt the chicken thoroughly the night before cooking, being sure to spread the salt into the cavity and under the skin. When you're ready to roast, preheat the oven to 450°F.

2. Drizzle the chicken with ½ tablespoon of the olive oil and then rub the oil and 2 tablespoons of the fresh herbs all over and under the skin.

3. Combine the cauliflower and broccoli in a large baking dish. Sprinkle on the remaining ½ tablespoon of olive oil and 1 tablespoon of herbs, plus the pepper and the remaining ¼ teaspoon of salt. Perch the chicken on top of the bed of vegetables and place the dish on the middle rack of the oven.

4. After 20 minutes, lower the heat to 375°F. Continue cooking for 30 to 40 minutes (depending on the size of the bird), or until the chicken's skin is thoroughly brown and crisp and a thermometer inserted into the thickest part of the thigh reads 165°F.

Nutrition Information (per serving): 402 calories, 33 g protein, 12 g carbohydrates, 5 g fiber, 4 g sugar, 26 g fat, 7 g saturated fat, 652 mg sodium

LIME CHICKEN

Prep Time: 10 minutes
Cook Time: 20 minutes
Total Time: 2 hours 30 minutes

SERVINGS: 4

Nothing reminds you of summer more than a citrusy chicken dish infused with warm-weather flavors like cilantro and lime. This dish is perfect for a poolside bash and would pair well with the Cucumber-Mint Smoothie on page 29.

½ cup lime juice

⅓ cup chopped fresh cilantro

¼ teaspoon salt

¼ teaspoon freshly ground black pepper

2 boneless, skinless chicken breasts

1 tablespoon extra-virgin olive oil

1. In a resealable plastic bag, combine the lime juice, cilantro, salt, and pepper. Rub the chicken with the oil and place it in the bag. Refrigerate for 2 hours.

2. Preheat the grill to medium-high and cook the chicken for about 10 minutes per side, or until a thermometer inserted in the thickest portion registers 160°F and the juices run clear. Serve immediately.

Nutrition Information (per serving): 137 calories, 24 g protein, 0 g carbohydrates, 0 g fiber, 0 g sugar, 3 g fat, 0.5 g saturated fat, 146 mg sodium

SPLIT CHICKEN

Prep Time: 15 minutes
Cook Time: 37 minutes
Total Time: 52 minutes

SERVINGS: 4

You can buy chicken halves, or if you'd rather halve it yourself, use a pair of poultry shears to cut out the backbone of a whole bird. You can leave the chicken connected at the breastbone if you have a pan large enough to hold it. If not, cut the chicken apart at the breastbone, too.

- 4 cloves garlic, minced
- 2 teaspoons marjoram
- 2 tablespoons extra-virgin olive oil, divided
- ¾ teaspoon salt, divided
- 1 chicken (3½ pounds), split in two
- 1 lemon, thinly sliced and seeds removed

1. Preheat the oven to 425°F. In a small bowl, stir together the garlic, marjoram, 1 tablespoon of the oil, and ½ teaspoon of the salt.

2. With your fingers, gently loosen the skin from the chicken, leaving the skin intact, and rub the marjoram mixture under the skin. Place the lemon slices under the skin.

3. In a very large ovenproof skillet, heat the remaining 1 tablespoon of oil over medium heat. Add the chicken and cook, skin side down, for 5 to 7 minutes, or until golden brown and lightly crisped. Turn the chicken over and sprinkle it with the remaining ¼ teaspoon of salt.

4. Cover just the chicken (but not the whole skillet) with foil and place a heavy ovenproof skillet on top. Place in the oven and roast for about 30 minutes, or until a thermometer inserted into the thickest part reads 165°F.

5. Transfer the chicken to a cutting board. Pour the pan juices into a bowl or gravy separator and remove the fat. Serve each person one-quarter of chicken with the degreased pan juices spooned over the top.

Nutrition Information (per serving): 634 calories, 49 g protein, 4 g carbohydrates, 2 g fiber, 0 g sugar, 46 g fat, 12 g saturated fat, 621 mg sodium

STEAK AND MUSHROOMS

Prep Time: 15 minutes
Cook Time: 12 minutes
Total Time: 30 minutes

SERVINGS: 4

Steak and mushrooms is a classic protein-packed dinner that can be changed up any number of ways. You can replace the rosemary with oregano or another dried herb. Or you can add 1 finely chopped scallion to the mushrooms before serving. If you prefer, you can broil or grill the beef instead of pan-frying it; just rub it with 1 to 2 teaspoons of olive oil before cooking.

1 boneless beef skirt steak or other cut (1½ pounds), ½" to ¾" thick

½ teaspoon freshly ground black pepper, divided

2 tablespoons extra-virgin olive oil, divided

10 ounces mushrooms, sliced

1 large clove garlic, minced

2 teaspoons minced fresh rosemary

¼ teaspoon salt

1. Season the beef with ¼ teaspoon of the pepper. Heat 1 tablespoon of the oil in a large, heavy skillet over high heat. Add the steak and cook for 3 to 4 minutes, or until it's deeply browned on the first side. Turn and cook for 5 to 7 minutes, or until it's well browned and a meat thermometer registers 145°F for medium.

2. Remove to a platter. Pour off the excess fat and add the remaining 1 tablespoon of oil to the skillet.

3. Reduce the heat to medium-low and add the mushrooms and garlic. Cook, stirring occasionally, for 2 to 4 minutes, or until the juices start to flow.

4. Add the rosemary, salt, and the remaining ¼ teaspoon of pepper. Cook for 2 to 3 minutes more, or until the mushrooms' juices have evaporated.

5. Remove from the heat. Stir in the beef juices that have accumulated on the platter. Serve the beef with the mushrooms.

Nutrition Information (per serving): 357 calories, 38 g protein, 3 g carbohydrates, 1 g fiber, 1 g sugar, 21 g fat, 6.5 g saturated fat, 263 mg sodium

FLANK STEAK

Prep Time: 8 minutes
Cook Time: 12 minutes
Total Time: 1 hour 20 minutes

SERVINGS: 4

1½ pounds (approx.) flank steak

¾ cup balsamic vinegar

1 tablespoon freshly ground black pepper

3 cloves garlic

⅓ cup extra-virgin olive oil

1. Pierce the steak all over with a fork to tenderize and allow for better absorption of the marinade.

2. Mix the vinegar, pepper, garlic, and oil in a large resealable plastic bag, reserving ¼ cup. Drop the steak into the bag and shake to coat. Put the bag in the refrigerator for at least an hour, or overnight.

3. Grill the steak over medium heat for about 6 minutes per side for medium rare. Baste with the reserved marinade.

4. Slice the meat diagonally across the grain in thin slices and drizzle with the remaining reserved marinade.

Nutrition Information (per serving): 346 calories, 36 g protein, 3 g carbohydrates, 0.5 g fiber, 2 g sugar, 20 g fat, 7 g saturated fat, 99 mg sodium

PEPPERED POT ROAST WITH SWEET POTATO WEDGES

Prep Time: 10 minutes
Cook Time: 32 minutes
Total Time: 1 hour

SERVINGS: 6

Sweet potatoes are teeming with vitamin A, fiber, and beta-carotene. In the grocery store, look for organic sweet potatoes. Conventional sweet potatoes are subjected to multiple rounds of fungicide and herbicide treatments, and you can't wash all the chemicals off.

2 teaspoons extra-virgin olive oil, divided

1 to 1¾ pounds trimmed top round roast

2 teaspoons freshly ground black pepper

½ teaspoon salt, divided

2 sweet potatoes, cut vertically into 8 wedges

1. Preheat the oven to 350°F. Rub 1 teaspoon of the oil evenly over the roast and season it with the pepper and ¼ teaspoon of the salt. Let it stand for 15 minutes.

2. Toss the sweet potatoes with the remaining 1 teaspoon of oil and ¼ teaspoon of salt.

3. Place a large nonstick, ovenproof skillet over medium-high heat. When it's hot, add the roast and sear it for 45 to 60 seconds per side, including the ends, or until just browned. Scatter the potato wedges around the roast.

4. Transfer the skillet to the oven and roast for 15 to 20 minutes, or until a thermometer inserted in the center registers 125°F for medium-rare. Remove the skillet from the oven and transfer the roast to a serving plate. Return the potatoes to the oven for about 10 minutes, or until they're browned and tender. Loosely place a piece of foil over the roast and let it stand while the potatoes finish cooking.

5. Slice the roast against the grain into thin slices and serve immediately, or refrigerate the whole roast and then slice very thinly by hand to use it as deli meat.

Nutrition Information (per serving): 160 calories, 25 g protein, 8 g carbohydrates, 2 g fiber, 2 g sugar, 5 g fat, 2 g saturated fat, 272 mg sodium

SIDES

Plentiful on the Plate

◄ SEARED CARROTS (page 120)

BUTTERNUT SQUASH WITH DRIED CHERRIES

Prep Time: 15 minutes
Cook Time: 40 minutes
Total Time: 55 minutes

SERVINGS: 8

Squash and cherries are a great flavor combo, and they're good for you, too. Compounds in cherries called anthocyanins—the same phytonutrients that give cherries their rich ruby hue—are powerful antioxidants that work to eliminate chronic pain. Like aspirin, cherries block inflammation and inhibit pain enzymes. This recipe makes 8 servings, so cut the ingredient quantities in half to serve 4.

8 cups 1" cubes butternut squash (about 4 pounds peeled, seeded, and cubed)

¾ cup dried cherries, chopped

2 tablespoons extra-virgin olive oil

1 teaspoon ground cumin

1 teaspoon kosher salt

½ teaspoon ground allspice

½ teaspoon ground coriander

¼ teaspoon freshly ground black pepper

2 tablespoons chopped parsley

1. Preheat the oven to 425°F.

2. In a large bowl, toss the squash and cherries with the oil.

3. In a small bowl, combine the cumin, salt, allspice, coriander, and pepper. Sprinkle the squash mixture with the spices and toss well to evenly coat.

4. Coat 2 baking sheets with cooking spray. Spread the squash in a single layer on the sheets and roast for 40 minutes, turning every 10 minutes. Serve immediately, sprinkled with parsley.

Nutrition Information (per serving): 140 calories, 2 g protein, 26 g carbohydrates, 4 g fiber, 9 g sugar, 4 g fat, 0.5 g saturated fat, 248 mg sodium

OVEN-ROASTED SWEET POTATOES

Prep Time: 10 minutes
Cook Time: 30 minutes
Total Time: 40 minutes

SERVINGS: 4

Don't go calling these orange sweet potatoes by any other name. Yams actually are not related to sweet potatoes and are rarely found in American grocery stores. Most of the "yams" you see in American supermarkets are actually sweet potatoes, which are cousins of morning glories.

2 medium sweet potatoes (1½ pounds), cut into 1" cubes

1½ tablespoons extra-virgin olive oil

½ teaspoon ground cinnamon

Salt

Freshly ground black pepper

1. Preheat the oven to 425°F. Coat a rimmed baking sheet with olive oil spray.

2. Arrange the sweet potatoes in a mound on the prepared baking sheet. Toss with the oil and cinnamon and season to taste with the salt and pepper.

3. Spread the potato cubes out on the baking sheet. Bake, stirring every 10 minutes, for about 30 minutes, or until tender. Serve immediately.

Nutrition Information (per serving): 176 calories, 3 g protein, 30 g carbohydrates, 5 g fiber, 9 g sugar, 5 g fat, 1 g saturated fat, 130 mg sodium

MASHED RUTABAGA WITH CARROTS

Prep Time: 15 minutes
Cook Time: 35 minutes
Total Time: 50 minutes

SERVINGS: 4

Rutabaga, a member of the turnip family, is super high in folate, which is known to lower the blood compounds that trigger artery inflammation and the risk of heart attack, stroke, and vascular disease. They have a sweet, complex flavor that's a perfect mashed-potato substitute. For a coarser version, use a potato masher.

1¾ pounds rutabaga, peeled, quartered, and thinly sliced

1 sweet potato, peeled and thinly sliced

½ pound carrots, thinly sliced

5 cloves garlic, peeled

1 bay leaf

½ teaspoon dried thyme

¼ teaspoon freshly ground black pepper

4 cups water

¾ teaspoon salt, divided

1 tablespoon extra-virgin olive oil

1. In a large saucepan, combine the rutabaga, potato, carrots, garlic, bay leaf, thyme, pepper, water, and ¼ teaspoon of the salt. Bring to a boil over medium heat and reduce to a simmer. Cover and cook for about 30 minutes, or until tender.

2. Reserving ½ cup of the cooking liquid, drain the vegetables. Discard the bay leaf.

3. With a potato masher, mash the vegetables along with the reserved cooking liquid and the oil.

4. Stir in the remaining ½ teaspoon of salt and serve immediately.

Nutrition Information (per serving): 147 calories, 3 g protein, 27 g carbohydrates, 7 g fiber, 11 g sugar, 4 g fat, 0.5 g saturated fat, 501 mg sodium

JICAMA FRIES

Prep Time: 15 minutes
Cook Time: 15 minutes
Total Time: 30 minutes

SERVINGS: 2

Underneath jicama's thick, brown skin is a crunchy, white flesh that tastes like a cross between a potato and a water chestnut. The perfect substitute for starchy, white potato French fries, jicama packs hefty doses of vitamin C and potassium.

1 pound jicama, peeled and cut into ¼"-thick wedges

1 tablespoon extra-virgin olive oil

1 clove garlic, cut and smashed

½ teaspoon sea salt

¼ teaspoon freshly ground black pepper

1. Preheat the oven to 450°F. Spread the jicama wedges on a baking sheet, drizzle the oil over the wedges, and mix with your hands to coat them evenly. Sprinkle the garlic over the jicama.

2. Bake for 15 minutes, or until the wedges are soft and beginning to char.

3. Sprinkle the fries with the salt and pepper. Serve immediately.

Nutrition Information (per serving): 142 calories, 2 g protein, 19 g carbohydrates, 10 g fiber, 4 g sugar, 7 g fat, 1 g saturated fat, 402 mg sodium

SPICED FENNEL

Prep Time: 10 minutes
Cook Time: 40 minutes
Total Time: 50 minutes

SERVINGS: 2

When you crave a flavor stronger than celery, try licorice-like fennel, a crunchy vegetable that has a white bulbous base and stalks that are topped by fronds that will remind you of dill. An added bonus: Fennel is packed with vitamin C and fiber. Keep the stalks to make chicken or vegetable stock, and use the fronds as tasty herbs added to a salad.

2 strips (2" long) orange zest

¾ teaspoon ground turmeric

1 tablespoon fresh thyme leaves

1 tablespoon extra-virgin olive oil

¼ teaspoon sea salt

3 large fennel bulbs (2½ pounds total), trimmed (fronds minced and 2 tablespoons reserved for garnish), cored, and cut into ¼"-thick slices

4 teaspoons fresh lemon juice

1. Preheat the oven to 325°F. Line a baking sheet with parchment paper.

2. Cut very thin slivers of the orange zest strips. In a large bowl, combine half of the orange zest, the turmeric, thyme, oil, and salt.

3. Add the sliced fennel to the bowl, toss to coat, and spread it out on the baking sheet. Roast, turning once halfway through, for 35 to 40 minutes, or until the fennel is tender.

4. In a small bowl, combine the lemon juice, the remaining orange zest, and the minced fennel fronds (if using). Add to the roasted fennel and toss to combine. Serve warm or at room temperature.

Nutrition Information (per serving): 196 calories, 5 g protein, 32 g carbohydrates, 13 g fiber, 1 g sugar, 8 g fat, 1 g saturated fat, 410 mg sodium

SAUTÉED JICAMA

Prep Time: 18 minutes
Cook Time: 12 minutes
Total Time: 30 minutes

SERVINGS: 4

When shopping for jicama, choose medium-size bulbs (smaller than 2 fists held together) without bruises. Here it's sautéed, which makes it both sweet and buttery. You can also eat it raw or swap it for water chestnuts in stir-fries, soups, and salads.

2 tablespoons extra-virgin olive oil

1 pound jicama, peeled, halved, and cut into thick matchsticks

1 carrot, cut into thick matchsticks

1 clove garlic, thinly sliced

⅓ cup water

Salt

1. Heat the oil in a large skillet over medium heat. Add the jicama, carrot, and garlic. Cook, stirring frequently, for about 7 minutes, or until the jicama is golden brown around the edges.

2. Add the water and cook for 3 to 5 minutes, or until the jicama and carrot are crisp-tender and the water has evaporated.

3. Season with salt to taste and serve immediately.

Nutrition Information (per serving): 110 calories, 1 g protein, 12 g carbohydrates, 6 g fiber, 3 g sugar, 7 g fat, 1 g saturated fat, 161 mg sodium

WARM LEEKS WITH LEMON-MUSTARD DRESSING

Prep Time: 15 minutes
Cook Time: 12 minutes
Total Time: 27 minutes

SERVINGS: 4

Leeks are the sophisticated members of the onion family. Their flavor is mild, with a slight earthiness. Bright green leaves are a sign of freshness; avoid those that are limp or yellowing. Make sure to clean leeks well, as they can be quite gritty.

1 bunch leeks (3 to 4), dark green tops discarded

1 tablespoon lemon juice

1 tablespoon extra-virgin olive oil

½ teaspoon Dijon mustard

¼ teaspoon salt

1. Cut the leeks in half lengthwise, then cut them into 2" pieces. Place the pieces in a large bowl of cool water and swish them around. Let them sit for a minute, then use your hands to scoop the leeks out without agitating the water. (The grit will sink to the bottom of the bowl.) Repeat 2 or 3 times, until the water remains clear.

2. Bring a large skillet of salted water to a simmer. Add the leeks and cook for 7 to 10 minutes, or until just tender. (Cooking time will vary depending upon the thickness of the leeks.) Drain well.

3. Meanwhile, in a large bowl, whisk together the lemon juice, oil, mustard, and salt. Add the drained but still-warm leeks to the dressing and toss to combine. Serve at room temperature.

Nutrition Information (per serving): 72 calories, 1 g protein, 10 g carbohydrates, 1 g fiber, 2 g sugar, 4 g fat, 0.5 g saturated fat, 174 mg sodium

MASHED SWEET POTATOES WITH HONEY

Prep Time: 5 minutes
Cook Time: 15 minutes
Total Time: 20 minutes

SERVINGS: 4

Sweet potatoes pack 438 percent of your daily value of infection-fighting vitamin A and are a major source of skin-protecting beta-carotene. Buy potatoes that are smooth, firm, and free of shriveled or dark areas. Store them in a cool, dry place—not in the refrigerator, which will rob the potatoes of their unique flavor.

1 pound sweet potatoes, peeled and cut into 1" chunks

¼ cup water

1 tablespoon honey

⅛ teaspoon ground cinnamon

Large pinch of freshly ground black pepper

1. In a medium saucepan, combine the sweet potatoes with enough cold water to cover them. Cover the pan and bring to a boil over high heat. Reduce the heat to medium-low and simmer for 12 to 15 minutes, or until the potatoes are fork-tender.

2. Meanwhile, in a small saucepan, warm the water, honey, cinnamon, and pepper over medium-low heat.

3. Drain the potatoes in a colander and return them to the medium saucepan.

4. Add the honey mixture. Mash until smooth and serve.

Nutrition Information (per serving): 79 calories, 2 g protein, 19 g carbohydrates, 2 g fiber, 9 g sugar, 0 g fat, 0 g saturated fat, 26 mg sodium

GARLIC-MARINATED MUSHROOMS TOPPED WITH AVOCADO

Prep Time: 10 minutes
Total Time: 20 minutes +
marinating time

SERVINGS: 8

Mushrooms, from button to shiitake, are immunity-boosting powerhouses. They increase the effectiveness of white blood cells, which are at the front line of your immune system. Marinated in garlic, another healing food, this side dish will get you back on your feet in no time if you're feeling under the weather.

1 pound mushrooms

½ cup extra-virgin olive oil

¼ cup vinegar

12 sprigs parsley, minced

3 cloves garlic, minced

¼ teaspoon freshly ground black pepper

2 Hass avocados

2 tablespoons lemon juice

¼ teaspoon salt

1 bunch watercress

Lemon wedges, for garnish

1. Stem the mushrooms.

2. In a large bowl, combine the oil, vinegar, parsley, garlic, and pepper and mix well.

3. Add the mushroom caps and turn to coat well. Cover and refrigerate overnight.

4. Halve the avocados and scoop the flesh into a medium bowl. With a fork or potato masher, mash the avocados with the lemon juice and salt. Add more lemon juice or salt if needed.

5. Remove the mushroom caps from the marinade. (Don't discard the marinade; it makes a perfectly nice salad dressing.) Fill each cap with avocado puree.

6. Line a serving platter with the watercress and arrange the mushrooms on top. Garnish with the lemon wedges and serve.

Nutrition Information (per serving): 100 calories, 3 g protein, 5 g carbohydrates, 3 g fiber, 1 g sugar, 9 g fat, 1 g saturated fat, 79 mg sodium

ROASTED BABY ARTICHOKES WITH ASPARAGUS

Prep Time: 20 minutes
Cook Time: 30 minutes
Total Time: 50 minutes

SERVINGS: 6

Baby artichokes pair especially well with olive oil and lemon. The spiky produce is actually a flower bud picked before it blooms. When trimmed and cooked, it has a mellow flavor that's slightly starchy.

24 baby artichokes

1 bunch asparagus (about 1 pound), trimmed

4 large shallots

2 tablespoons extra-virgin olive oil

1 cup sugar snap peas

½ teaspoon kosher salt

¼ teaspoon freshly ground black pepper

2 teaspoons fresh thyme leaves

1 cup low-sodium chicken broth

1 lemon

1. Heat the oven to 400°F.

2. Clean and drain the artichokes and pat them dry. Halve baby artichokes lengthwise; cut larger ones into quarters lengthwise. Halve the asparagus spears. Peel the shallots and slice them lengthwise into 2" pieces.

3. Place the oil in a 12-inch ovenproof skillet over medium-high heat. Add the artichokes and cook, stirring, for 2 minutes.

4. Add the snap peas, asparagus, and shallots and sauté for about 3 minutes, or until the artichoke edges are golden. Season to taste with salt and pepper.

5. Add the thyme and chicken broth and bring to a boil.

6. Transfer the skillet to the oven. Roast, turning once or twice, for 20 to 25 minutes, or until the artichokes are just tender. (Check halfway through. Add a little water if the broth has evaporated.)

7. Remove from the oven and serve with lemon wedges.

Nutrition Information (per serving): 168 calories, 10 g protein, 30 g carbohydrates, 10 g fiber, 6 g sugar, 5 g fat, 1 g saturated fat, 397 mg sodium

CREAMED SPINACH WITH MUSHROOMS

Prep Time: 12 minutes
Cook Time: 15 minutes
Total Time: 27 minutes

SERVINGS: 4

We've come a long way since the time when cookbooks directed that spinach be "stewed" for half an hour, turning it into a gray mush with little nutritional value. When spinach is cooked just long enough to wilt, the leaves stay a vibrant green and few nutrients are lost.

2 large shallots or 1 small onion, chopped

¼ cup chicken broth, divided

¾ teaspoon extra-virgin olive oil

4 ounces small mushrooms, quartered

1 pound spinach, tough stems removed

⅛ teaspoon salt

⅛ teaspoon freshly ground black pepper

1. In a large nonstick skillet, combine the shallots, 2 tablespoons of the broth, and the oil. Cook over medium-high heat, stirring constantly, for 3 to 4 minutes, or until the shallots are softened.

2. Add the mushrooms and the remaining 2 tablespoons of broth. Cook, stirring frequently, for 4 to 6 minutes, or until the mushrooms are softened.

3. Increase the heat to high. Add the spinach by handfuls and stir constantly until it wilts. Cook for 1 minute after wilting, season with the salt and pepper, and serve immediately.

Nutrition Information (per serving): 65 calories, 5 g protein, 11 g carbohydrates, 3 g fiber, 1 g sugar, 2 g fat, 0 g saturated fat, 147 mg sodium

SEARED CARROTS

Prep Time: 5 minutes
Cook Time: 12 minutes
Total Time: 17 minutes

SERVINGS: 2

Thanks to their natural sugar, carrots are a deliciously sweet snack that comes packaged with vitamins, minerals, and fiber. They're also abundant in falcarinol—a phytochemical that may help protect you against colon cancer—as well as vitamin A, which provides vision-boosting nutrients.

1 pound young whole carrots

1 tablespoon extra-virgin olive oil

¼ teaspoon fine sea salt

¼ teaspoon ground cumin

¼ teaspoon ground coriander

Pinch of freshly ground black pepper

1. Place a steamer basket in a large pot with 1" to 2" of water. Bring to a boil over high heat. Steam the carrots in the basket for about 5 minutes, or until just tender. Remove from the heat.

2. Heat the oil in a medium skillet over medium-low heat.

3. Add the salt, cumin, coriander, and pepper and swirl the mixture in the pan for a minute.

4. Add the carrots, toss them to coat, and allow them to cook in the mixture for 3 minutes. Serve immediately.

Nutrition Information (per serving): 158 calories, 2 g protein, 22 g carbohydrates, 7 g fiber, 11 g sugar, 8 g fat, 1 g saturated fat, 354 mg sodium

ROASTED BRUSSELS SPROUTS AND ONIONS WITH THYME

Prep Time: 14 minutes
Cook Time: 25 minutes
Total Time: 39 minutes

SERVINGS: 4

Buying Vidalia or Walla Walla onions, which don't have strong vapors, could reduce your risk of crying while chopping. Not an option? Try cutting the bulb under water or chilling the onion in the refrigerator, which can slow the chemical reactions that release pungent fumes.

1½ pounds fresh Brussels sprouts

1 large sweet white onion, quartered and cut into ½"-thick slices

1 tablespoon extra-virgin olive oil

4 teaspoons fresh thyme leaves

¼ teaspoon salt

Pinch of freshly ground black pepper

1. Preheat the oven to 400°F. Set out a rimmed baking sheet.

2. Trim the yellowed leaves and the ends from the sprouts. Cut each into quarters or halves, if they're small.

3. Place the sprouts on the baking sheet and toss them with the onion, oil, thyme, salt, and pepper.

4. Roast for 20 to 25 minutes, stirring 2 or 3 times, until the vegetables are tender and lightly browned.

Nutrition Information (per serving): 131 calories, 7 g protein, 22 g carbohydrates, 7 g fiber, 8 g sugar, 4 g fat, 1 g saturated fat, 195 mg sodium

LEMON BROCCOLI

Prep Time: 10 minutes
Cook Time: 7 minutes
Total Time: 17 minutes

SERVINGS: 4

A single stalk of this cruciferous all-star vegetable packs 3 grams of protein—about as much as an ounce of chicken breast. Eat 1 cup, and you'll get a hearty dose of calcium, as well as manganese, potassium, phosphorus, magnesium, and iron.

1 medium-size head broccoli

¼ cup lemon juice or 1 teaspoon extra-virgin olive oil

Lemon wedges

1. Trim the florets from the broccoli stems and cut them into bite-size pieces.

2. Place a steamer basket in a large pot with 1" to 2" of water. Bring to a boil over high heat. Steam the broccoli in the basket for 5 minutes, or until crisp-tender.

3. Drain well. Toss the broccoli with the lemon juice or oil. Serve with lemon wedges.

Nutrition Information (per serving): 51 calories, 4 g protein, 11 g carbohydrates, 3 g fiber, 2 g sugar, 1 g fat, 0 g saturated fat, 50 mg sodium

GLAZED TURNIPS, PEARL ONIONS, AND CARROTS

Prep Time: 15 minutes
Cook Time: 33 minutes
Total Time: 48 minutes

SERVINGS: 4

Flavorful enough for Thanksgiving dinner, yet easy enough for any night of the week, this attractive trio of vegetables also contains a powerful mix of complex carbohydrates and fiber. Plus, turnips are a good source of the mineral manganese, which helps regulate blood sugar.

- 4 peeled turnips (¾ pound total), cut into 8 wedges each
- 2 cups frozen small white onions (about 10 ounces), thawed
- 1 cup baby carrots
- 1¼ cups chicken broth
- 2 tablespoons balsamic vinegar
- 2 tablespoons extra-virgin olive oil
- ½ teaspoon ground cumin
- ¼ teaspoon sea salt
- ⅛ teaspoon freshly ground black pepper
- 2 tablespoons chopped fresh parsley

1. In a large skillet over medium-high heat, combine the turnips, onions, carrots, broth, vinegar, oil, cumin, salt, and pepper.

2. Bring to a boil, then reduce the heat to medium and simmer, stirring occasionally, for 20 to 25 minutes, or until the liquid evaporates.

3. Continue cooking, stirring often, for 4 to 6 minutes, or until the vegetables are golden and shiny. Remove from the heat and stir in the parsley. Serve immediately.

Nutrition Information (per serving): 143 calories, 2 g protein, 17 g carbohydrates, 4 g fiber, 10 g sugar, 7 g fat, 1 g saturated fat, 544 mg sodium

ROASTED BEETS WITH HERBS AND GARLIC

Prep Time: 10 minutes
Cook Time: 1 hour
Total Time: 1 hour 10 minutes

SERVINGS: 4

Think of beets as red spinach. Just like Popeye's power food, this crimson vegetable is one of the best sources of both folate and betaine. They work to lower your blood levels of homocysteine, an inflammatory compound that can damage your arteries and increase your risk of heart disease.

2 pounds small beets, scrubbed

2 tablespoons chicken or vegetable broth

1 tablespoon extra-virgin olive oil

2 cloves garlic, minced

1 large shallot, finely chopped

½ teaspoon dried sage, crushed

Pinch of salt

Pinch of freshly ground black pepper

1. Preheat the oven to 400°F.

2. Cut each beet into 8 wedges. Place the beets, broth, oil, garlic, shallot, sage, salt, and pepper in an 11" x 7" baking dish. Toss to coat well.

3. Cover tightly with foil and bake, stirring occasionally, for 1 hour, or until the beets are very tender, and serve.

Nutrition Information (per serving): 136 calories, 4 g protein, 23 g carbohydrates, 7 g fiber, 16 g sugar, 4 g fat, 0.5 g saturated fat, 280 mg sodium

GREEN BEANS AND CARROTS

Prep Time: 10 minutes
Cook Time: 12 minutes
Total Time: 22 minutes

SERVINGS: 4

Who knew that something as quick and simple as green beans and carrots could be such a tasty side dish? Toss with a little bit of oil for a delicious accompaniment to chicken or fish, or chow down on these delightful veggies solo for a tasty midday snack.

4 carrots, cut into 3" matchsticks

1 package (8 to 10 ounces) frozen whole green beans

1 tablespoon canola oil

1. Place a steamer basket in a large pot with 1" to 2" of water. Bring to a boil over high heat. Place the carrots and green beans in the basket and steam for about 10 minutes, or until tender.

2. Drain, toss with the oil, and serve immediately.

Nutrition Information (per serving): 71 calories, 1 g protein, 9 g carbohydrates, 3 g fiber, 5 g sugar, 4 g fat, 0.5 g saturated fat, 43 mg sodium

ASPARAGUS WITH BALSAMIC VINEGAR

Prep Time: 5 minutes
Cook Time: 10 minutes
Total Time: 15 minutes

SERVINGS: 4

Asparagus is a delicious alternative to starches as a side for fish or poultry, and it is loaded with bone-protecting vitamin K. It's also rich in folate, which may help ward off heart disease and reduce your risk of obesity.

1 bunch asparagus, woody ends removed

1 tablespoon extra-virgin olive oil

¼ teaspoon salt

¼ teaspoon freshly ground black pepper

1½ teaspoons balsamic vinegar

1. Preheat the oven to 400°F.

2. In a large bowl, toss the asparagus with the oil, salt, and pepper. Arrange it in a single layer on a baking sheet.

3. Roast the asparagus for about 10 minutes, until it's soft (not mushy) and lightly brown. Drizzle with the vinegar. Serve immediately.

Nutrition Information (per serving): 46 calories, 1 g protein, 3 g carbohydrates, 1 g fiber, 1 g sugar, 4 g fat, 0.5 g saturated fat, 147 mg sodium

SQUASH RIBBONS

Prep Time: 10 minutes
Cook Time: 12 minutes
Total Time: 22 minutes

SERVINGS: 4

Like cucumbers, zucchini are a low-calorie favorite. They're high in riboflavin, a B vitamin needed for red blood cell production and for converting carbohydrates into energy. A large zucchini provides 27 percent of your daily requirement.

2 medium (9-ounce) zucchini

2 medium (6-ounce) yellow squash

1 tablespoon extra-virgin olive oil

2 teaspoons minced shallot

½ teaspoon salt + more to taste

Freshly ground black pepper

2 teaspoons freshly chopped basil

2 teaspoons finely chopped oregano leaves

1. Halve each zucchini and yellow squash lengthwise. Use a teaspoon to scoop out the seeds. Cut off the neck and rounded blossom end, then slice the squash lengthwise into ¼" strips to make long, thin ribbons. Discard the outermost strips that are mainly skin.

2. In a medium skillet, heat the oil over medium heat. Add the shallot and cook for 1 minute, or until soft. Add the squash and sprinkle with the ½ teaspoon of salt. Cook, stirring occasionally, for 3 minutes, or until the squash looks moist.

3. Increase the heat to medium-high and cook, stirring constantly, for 8 minutes, or until tender. The pieces should bend easily but still be tender-crisp.

4. Using tongs, remove the squash to a serving plate. Spoon the shallots from the pan over the squash and season with salt and pepper to taste. Sprinkle on the basil and oregano and serve immediately.

Nutrition Information (per serving): 73 calories, 3 g protein, 9 g carbohydrates, 3 g fiber, 5 g sugar, 4 g fat, 1 g saturated fat, 91 mg sodium

SALT AND PEPPER KALE CHIPS

Prep Time: 10 minutes
Cook Time: 15 minutes
Total Time: 25 minutes

SERVINGS: 2

When the crunchy cravings hit, you need something better for your body than salty, bloat-inducing potato chips. Try these crispy kale chips, which are low in calories, high in nutrition, and made from real veggies—and little else.

6 cups coarsely chopped kale, tough ribs removed

2 teaspoons grape seed oil

¼ teaspoon fine sea salt

¼ teaspoon freshly ground black pepper

1. Heat the oven to 350°F. Lightly coat 2 baking sheets with cooking spray or line them with parchment paper.

2. Place the kale in a large bowl. Drizzle with the grape seed oil and sprinkle with salt. Use your hands to toss the kale until it's evenly coated.

3. Arrange the kale in a single layer on the baking sheet. Bake for 10 minutes.

4. Remove the baking sheet from the oven and turn the kale chips over. Return the baking sheet to the oven and bake for 5 minutes, or until the kale chips are crispy.

5. Sprinkle with the pepper. Serve immediately.

Nutrition Information (per serving): 139 calories, 9 g protein, 18 g carbohydrates, 4 g fiber, 0 g sugar, 6 g fat, 0.5 g saturated fat, 316 mg sodium

ROSEMARY SWEET POTATO WEDGES

Prep Time: 10 minutes
Cook Time: 22 minutes
Total Time: 32 minutes

SERVINGS: 4

Skip the home fries and try these sweet potato wedges, instead. Baked in the oven, they are packed with beta-carotene and are lower in fat than a fried potato—but they still have a satisfyingly crisp skin. Cut the wedges even thinner for a bigger crunch.

2 tablespoons extra-virgin olive oil

1 tablespoon chopped fresh rosemary or 2 teaspoons dried

3 medium sweet potatoes

1 teaspoon salt + more to taste

¼ teaspoon freshly ground black pepper + more to taste

1. Preheat the oven to 450°F. Place the oil in a small saucepan over medium heat. Stir in the rosemary and cook for 1 minute, or until fragrant. Remove from the heat and strain out the rosemary.

2. Cut the sweet potatoes lengthwise into 1½"-thick wedges and place them in a large bowl. Season with the salt and pepper and drizzle with the oil mixture. Toss gently.

3. Arrange the wedges in a single layer on a large baking sheet, leaving space between them. Bake in the upper third of the oven for 20 minutes, turning once, or until the potatoes are softened and lightly browned.

4. Season again with salt and pepper to taste and carefully remove the wedges from the sheet. (They're relatively fragile after cooking.) Serve immediately.

Nutrition Information (per serving): 195 calories, 2 g protein, 20 g carbohydrates, 3 g fiber, 4 g sugar, 13 g fat, 5 g saturated fat, 636 mg sodium

BASIL-MINT SUGAR SNAPS

Prep Time: 5 minutes
Cook Time: 12 minutes
Total Time: 17 minutes

SERVINGS: 4

Mint, basil, and lime give these crisp-tender beans a bright, refreshing flavor. If you would prefer, you can also make this snappy side dish with just basil, which is loaded with natural anti-inflammatory, antioxidant, and anticancer effects.

1½ pounds sugar snap peas, strings removed

¼ cup chopped fresh mint

¼ cup chopped fresh basil

1 tablespoon extra-virgin olive oil

1 tablespoon fresh lime juice

¾ teaspoon salt

1. Place a steamer basket in a large pot with 1" to 2" of water. Bring to a boil over high heat. Steam the peas in the basket for 5 to 10 minutes, or until crisp-tender.

2. Transfer the peas to a large bowl and add the mint, basil, oil, lime juice, and salt.

3. Toss to combine, then serve immediately.

Nutrition Information (per serving): 104 calories, 5 g protein, 14 g carbohydrates, 5 g fiber, 7 g sugar, 4 g fat, 1 g saturated fat, 444 mg sodium

CARROTS AND ZUCCHINI WITH CILANTRO

Prep Time: 10 minutes
Cook Time: 17 minutes
Total Time: 27 minutes

SERVINGS: 8

When you cut vegetables into same-size strips, or matchsticks, about 3" long, the technique is called "julienne." Peel the vegetable and cut from the fatter end first. Trim it into a rectangular block and place the block on its side. Cut ⅛"-wide slices lengthwise, and you've julienned.

1 pound carrots, cut into matchsticks

3 medium zucchini, cut into matchsticks

½ cup chopped cilantro or parsley

½ teaspoon salt

¼ teaspoon freshly ground black pepper

1. Place a steamer basket in a large pot with 1" to 2" of water. Bring to a boil over high heat. Steam the carrots in the basket for about 10 minutes, or until crisp-tender.

2. Add the zucchini to the mix and steam for 5 minutes. (Or, if your steamer isn't big enough, steam the zucchini separately.)

3. Transfer the vegetables to a large bowl, toss them with the cilantro, salt, and pepper, and serve.

Nutrition Information (per serving): 36 calories, 1 g protein, 8 g carbohydrates, 2 g fiber, 4 g sugar, 0 g fat, 0 g saturated fat, 191 mg sodium

A Week of Meals
to Feed Body and Soul

This 7-day meal plan is an opportunity to get in tune with your body's essential nutrients and energy needs. No, this isn't a strict diet and weight-loss program. As a matter of fact, this is not calorie restrictive at all. This plan is just a guideline; we encourage you to mix and match meals, to experiment with new flavors, and most importantly, to have fun!

A Week of Meals to Feed Body and Soul is a healing and elimination program, and it will help you discover what foods you're sensitive to and therefore what triggers you should avoid in the future. Before you begin, take note of the Shopping List on page 140. This is where you'll find approved foods, and foods that shouldn't touch your plate. This program is designed to include only the ingredients proven to reduce inflammation and heal your body by removing toxic substances, junk foods, high-allergen foods (such as grains and especially gluten), and dairy. If you have weight to lose, you may see that you drop a few pounds over the next 7 days, as many who follow the plan do. If you have hyperthyroid symptoms and are worried about losing weight, make sure to eat enough healing proteins, carbohydrates, and fats each day. Many hyperthyroid sufferers on the plan, for example, have found that eating sweet potatoes helps them keep weight on. (Find our recipe for Oven-Roasted Sweet Potatoes on page 106.)

In order for this program to be as effective as possible, you need to be prepared. Rid your cabinets of any and all foods that could tempt you into deviating from the plan, and keep plenty of fresh fruits and vegetables on hand for snacking. Once you start cooking, make sure to note how many servings the recipe makes. Many of the meals, such as the hearty Baby Artichoke Stew on page 37, feed four or even six people, so plan accordingly if you're only cooking for one or two, and make sure to store the rest for another day.

Try to drink at least 64 ounces of pure, filtered water each day. You can also pair any of your meals with organic green or herbal tea and organic, unsweetened cranberry juice. For example, the Grilled Peaches on page 11 pair well with a soothing cup of green tea.

It's super important to keep a journal this week. You don't need to spend a lot of time doing this—you might just jot down notes of what you ate, when you ate it, and how it made you feel. This will make it much easier for you to see any positive or negative reactions you had to eating (or eliminating!)

certain foods. By optimizing your nutrition, you're preparing your body to become healthier than ever. Approach the next 7 days with an open mind, a fully stocked pantry, and a hearty appetite for change.

SHOPPING LIST

This shopping list includes foods for the following meal plan as well as foods to eat while following Michelle Corey's *The Thyroid Cure* autoimmune healing program. When you are in the beginning phase of that program and are still determining your level of food sensitivity, do not eat sugar. Otherwise, a small amount of organic honey is acceptable in teas and salad dressings, as long as you are sure you don't react to it. Please keep it to no more than 1 teaspoon per day.

Organic Fruits: Apples, avocados, blackberries, blueberries, cherries, coconuts, lemons, nectarines, peaches, pears, plums, pomegranates, raspberries

Organic Vegetables: Artichokes, arugula, asparagus, bok choy, broccoli, Brussels sprouts, cabbage, cauliflower, celery, chard, collard greens, cucumbers, fennel, kale, leeks, lettuce, rhubarb, spinach, squash, watercress

Healing Roots: Beets, carrots, celeriac, jicama, onions, parsnips, radishes, rutabagas, shallots, sweet potatoes, turnips, yams

Healing Proteins: Organic, omega-3-enriched eggs; organic, lean meats, such as beef, buffalo, and lamb; organic poultry, such as chicken, game hen, pheasant, and turkey; wild-caught fish, such as salmon or trout; soaked and sprouted nuts and seeds; hypoallergenic rice protein powder

Healing Fats: Avocado, borage oil, coconut oil, ghee, olive oil

Dairy Substitutes: Coconut kefir, coconut milk, coconut yogurt

Healing Herbs: Basil, bay leaves, chamomile, chives, cilantro, cumin, dill, lavender, lemon balm, lemongrass, marjoram, mint, oregano, parsley, peppermint, rosemary, saffron, sage, spearmint, tarragon, thyme

Spices and Sweeteners: Cinnamon, cloves, garlic, ginger, onion powder, saffron, sea salt, stevia, turmeric, organic honey

Pantry Items: Coconut flakes, coconut flour, olives, organic apple-cider vinegar, canned salmon

Fermented Foods: Coconut kefir, coconut yogurt (if you are not making the homemade recipe on page 31), fermented vegetables, kimchi (without nightshades), kombucha, sauerkraut

Drinks: Drink at least 64 ounces of pure, filtered water each day; organic green tea; organic, diluted, unsweetened cranberry juice; organic herbal tea; Teeccino coffee substitute; Dandy Blend coffee substitute

FOODS TO AVOID

Protein: Pork, canned meats, uncooked meats, cured or processed meats (such as cold cuts, sausage, hot dogs), sushi, shellfish, and crustaceans.

Dairy: All animal milks, including cow, goat, and sheep; cheese; yogurt and kefir; cottage cheese; butter; ice cream

Grains: Amaranth, barley, buckwheat, bulgur, corn, farro, kamut, millet, oats, quinoa (not technically a grain, but excluded), rice, rye, sorghum, spelt, teff, wheat (All grains and products made from grains must be eliminated; the exception is organic brown rice if you know you don't react to it. So must all refined white flour products, such as macaroni and cheese, cookies, cakes, pizza dough, pasta, tortillas, pancake and waffle mixes, and cookies, as well as the carbs in the ingredients of many "low-carb" products.)

Nuts and Seeds: Almonds, Brazil nuts, coffee, cocoa, hazelnuts, pecans, macadamias, walnuts, hemp, canola, caraway, chia, coriander, cumin, fennel seeds, fenugreek, mustard, nutmeg, poppy, pumpkin, sesame, sunflower

Grasses: Alfalfa, barley grass, oat grass, wheatgrass

Fruits: Grapefruit, grapes, melons, oranges and orange juice, strawberries, tropical fruits

Beans and Legumes: Adzuki beans, black beans, black-eyed peas, chickpeas, fava beans, kidney beans, lentils, lima beans, peanuts, soybeans

Nightshades: Ground red pepper, chile peppers, eggplant, goji berries, ground cherries, habaneros, jalapeños, paprika, poblanos, potatoes (all forms, but especially chips), sweet peppers (green, red, and yellow), tomatoes, tomatillos

Sweeteners: Sugar in all forms—brown, white, or in the raw; honey; sugar alcohols (xylitol); artificial sweeteners (Equal, Splenda, Sweet'N Low); agave; evaporated cane juice; fructose; glucose; high-fructose corn syrup; maple syrup; sucrose

Condiments and Dressings: Conventionally pickled (not fermented) foods, bottled salad dressings, ketchup, relish, mayonnaise, BBQ sauce, teriyaki (If it comes in a bottle and contains salt, sugar, thickening agents, or any other potentially compromising additives, avoid it.)

Drinks: Alcohol, caffeinated drinks (coffee, energy drinks), concentrated fruit juices, soft drinks

Fats: Butter and butter substitutes, canola oil, margarine, processed oils, excess dietary fats (especially trans fats)

ANYTHING YOU ALREADY KNOW YOU REACT TO

Performance bars, drinks, and gels, and protein shakes

MEAL PLANS

DAY 1

Breakfast
Smoked Salmon Breakfast Scramble (page 18)

Midmorning
Fruit Bowl with Avocado (page 8)

Lunch
Spring Rice Bowl with Asparagus (page 60)

Midafternoon
Salt and Pepper Kale Chips (page 133)

Dinner
Lamb Lollipops (page 81) with Glazed Turnips, Pearl Onions, and Carrots (page 124)

DAY 2

Breakfast
Savory Rice Porridge (page 7)

Midmorning
Blueberry Smoothie (page 25)

Lunch
Chilled Carrot Soup (page 44)

Midafternoon
Jicama Fries (page 108)

Dinner
Lemon Caper Halibut (page 77) with Lemon Broccoli (page 123)

DAY 3

Breakfast
Avocado Egg Boat (page 23)

Midmorning
Green Smoothie (page 26)

Lunch
Balsamic Beets (page 50)

Midafternoon
Mashed Rutabaga with Carrots (page 107)

Dinner
Lime Chicken (page 96) with Squash Ribbons (page 130)

DAY 4

Breakfast
Asparagus and Mushroom Rice Bowl (page 21)

Midmorning
Honeyed Summer Fruit Bowl (page 6)

Lunch
Thai Squash Soup (page 47)

Midafternoon
Basil-Mint Sugar Snaps (page 137)

Dinner
Plank Salmon with Green Beans (page 73)

DAY 5

Breakfast

Sweet Potato Pancakes (page 12)

Midmorning

Coconut Yogurt with Raspberries
(page 5)

Lunch

Simple Buffalo Burgers (page 58)

Midafternoon

Brussels Sprouts Slaw with Beef
(page 57)

Dinner

Split Chicken (page 97) with Green
Beans and Carrots (page 126)

DAY 6

Breakfast

The New American Omelet (page 15)

Midmorning

Raspberry Smoothie (page 30)

Lunch

Curry-Spiced Roasted Cauliflower
(page 67)

Midafternoon

Carrots and Zucchini with Cilantro
(page 138)

Dinner

Lamb and Asparagus (page 84)

DAY 7

Breakfast

Grilled Steak and Eggs (page 17)

Midmorning

Coconut Yogurt with Blackberries
(page 2)

Lunch

Roasted Butternut Squash Skewers with
Rosemary Dip (page 61)

Midafternoon

Spiced Fennel (page 111)

Dinner

Trout with Cabbage (page 79)

INDEX

Boldface page numbers indicate photographs.

A

Almond-Encrusted Wild Salmon with Greens, **62**, 63
Almond sprouts
    Almond-Encrusted Wild Salmon with Greens, **62**, 63
Anchovy fillets
    Tapenade, for Herb-Marinated Lamb Chops, 82–83
Apple juice
    Chilled Carrot Soup, 44, **45**
Apples, cooking
    Country Coleslaw, 56
    Fall Squash Soup, 36
Apples, Granny Smith
    Roasted Chicken Breasts with Sautéed Cabbage and
        Apples, 92
Applesauce
    Sweet Potato Pancakes, 12, **13**
Artichokes, baby, 37
    Baby Artichoke Stew, 37
    Roasted Baby Artichokes with Asparagus, 116, **117**
Arugula
    Balsamic Beets, **32**, 50
    Lamb and Asparagus, 84
Asparagus, 21, 129
    Asparagus and Mushroom Rice Bowl, **viii**, 21
    Asparagus with Balsamic Vinegar, **128**, 129
    Baby Artichoke Stew, 37
    Chicken Stir-Fry, 68, **69**
    Italian Chicken and Vegetables, 93
    Lamb and Asparagus, 84
    New American Omelet, The, **14**, 15
    Poached Salmon with Vegetables, 75
    Roasted Baby Artichokes with Asparagus, 116, **117**
    Spring Rice Bowl with Asparagus, 60
Asparagus and Mushroom Rice Bowl, **viii**, 21
Asparagus with Balsamic Vinegar, **128**, 129
Avocado Egg Boat, 23
Avocados
    Avocado Egg Boat, 23
    Chilled Avocado and Cucumber Soup, 40

    Fruit Bowl with Avocado, 8, **9**
    Garlic-Marinated Mushrooms Topped with Avocado,
        115
    Salmon with Avocado Salsa, 74

B

Baby Artichoke Stew, 37
Baked Salmon, 64, **65**
Balsamic Beets, **32**, 50
Basil
    Basil-Mint Sugar Snaps, **136**, 137
    Fruit Bowl with Avocado, 8, **9**
    Thai Beef Salad with Mint, **52**, 53
Basil-Mint Sugar Snaps, **136**, 137
Bay leaves, 90
    Tuscan Country Chicken, 90, **91**
Beans, dried, 141
Beans, green (snap)
    Chicken Stir-Fry, 68, **69**
    Green Beans and Carrots, 126, **127**
    New American Omelet, The, **14**, 15
    Plank Salmon with Green Beans, **72**, 73
Beef, 17, 57
Beef, chuck
    Beef Stew with Root Vegetables, 38–39, **39**
Beef, flank steak
    Flank Steak, 99
Beef, ground
    Cabbage and Beef Soup, 41
Beef, round
    Root Vegetable Soup, 43
Beef, sirloin steak
    Beef Skewers with Grilled Vegetables, 54, **55**
    Grilled Steak and Eggs, 17
Beef, skirt steak
    Steak and Mushrooms, 98
Beef, strip steak
    Thai Beef Salad with Mint, **52**, 53